He She They Us

QUEER POEMS

Charlie Castelletti

MACMILLAN

Published 2024 by Macmillan Children's Books
an imprint of Pan Macmillan
The Smithson, 6 Briset Street, London EC1M 5NR
EU representative: Macmillan Publishers Ireland Ltd, 1st Floor,
The Liffey Trust Centre, 117–126 Sheriff Street Upper
Dublin 1, D01 YC43
Associated companies throughout the world
www.panmacmillan.com

ISBN 978-1-0350-3427-7

1 3 5 7 9 8 6 4 2

A CIP catalogue record for this book is available from the British Library.

Printed and bound by CPI Group (UK) Ltd, Croydon CR0 4YY

To all of us

Contents

Introduction   xv

Moments   **1**

Episode of Hands	Hart Crane	3
We Two Boys together Clinging	Walt Whitman	5
A Football Player	Edward Cracroft Lefroy	6
A Room of Firsts	Karl Knights	7
Mark[1] the Second[2]	Alton Melvar M Dapanas	9
Romance	Claude McKay	10
Reminiscence	Olive Custance	11
Demonstration	Jack Cooper	12
Rain Kiss	Freja Nicole Woolf	13
A Renewal	James Merrill	16
Flight	Kae Tempest	17
On the Stairs	C. P. Cavafy	18
Glimpse	Andrew McMillan	19
Invisible Boy	Matthew Haigh	21
The Trick	David Ly	24
Natural Habitat	Kelsey Day	25

Scenes   29

The Gallery Floor   Erica Gillingham   31
To Lallie (Outside the British
    Museum)   Amy Levy   32
A Wall Flower   Amy Levy   35
Skin Tags   Karl Knights   36
Things That Are Rare   Richie Hofmann   37
Boys in Moonlight Shine   Gregory Woods   38
After Sunday Lunch   Gregory Woods   39
Jesus at the Gay Bar   Jay Hulme   40
Can a thunderstorm happen in
    mid-winter . . .   Sophia Parnok   41
On the Road to the Sea   Charlotte Mew   42
Girl Guides   Jo Morris Dixon   45
To the Girl at the Bus Stop   Nikita Gill   46
Words and Music   Colette Bryce   47
Queer   Robert Hamberger   48

We Are Strong   51

Dysphoria   Oliver Baez Bendorf   53
The Ride That Loops Infinitely/
    Tall Bed Above Water   Rainie Oet   54
#131 Lapras   Winter Chen   56
Reconciliation   Luís Costa   57
The Moon is Trans   Joshua Jennifer Espinoza   58
All the Dead Boys Look Like Me   Christopher Soto   60
A Shropshire Lad   A. E. Housman   63

Eating Slurs for Breakfast   Elspeth Wilson   64
All Trains Are Going Local   Timothy Liu   65
Today I Love Being Alive   Alex Dimitrov   66
Elegy   Harry Josephine Giles   67
Don't Die   Jay Hulme   70
If I could pray the gay away   Andrés N. Ordorica   72
"Hope" is the thing with feathers   Emily Dickinson   73
A Litany for Survival   Audre Lorde   74

Queer Joy   **77**
Rainbow Road   Rainie Oet   79
In Sims, I Woohoo with a Girl   Elspeth Wilson   80
playtime   Jo Morris Dixon   81
school bell ring   Hope Ndaba   82
Iced Coffee   Charlotte Moore   84
Ringing in Sick to Go Mermaid
    Hunting   Sarah Clancy   85
Having a Coke with You   Frank O'Hara   87
Immanence   Micheál McCann   89
Of Course He Smells Like Lemons   Luís Costa   90
from The Great Lover   Rupert Brooke   91
Sun catcher, record player   Charlie Morris   93
Spout   John McCullough   95
Sheep's Head Peninsula   Rosamund Taylor   96
Mango Kiss   Erica Gillingham   97
Leftovers   Eva Griffin   99
syntax   Maureen N. McLane   100

Something Rhymed   Jackie Kay   101
An ode to trans bodies   Cal Brantley   103

Identity   **107**

1D3N+1+Y   Winter Chen   108
Exqueerience   Phoebe Trott   110
You didn't go to prom with me   Caitlin Tina Jones   112
Mirror Boy   Jaime Lock   113
On the Run   Nicoletta Poungias   115
Not Your GBF   Louis Glazzard   116
Red, Red, Red   Andrés N. Ordorica   117
Playground Games   Aaron Cawood   120
Shaping Staff   Toby Buckley   121
60% of bisexual people are in
     psychological distress at any
     one time   Elspeth Wilson   122
Gender Keeps Me Up at Night   Sasha Torchinsky   123
Seahorse   Charlie Castelletti   124
Top Surgery   William Keohane   125
My Gender   Jason Purcell   126
A Love Affair with
     They/Them/Theirs   Brody Parrish Craig   127
My Gender is not a Controversial
     Topic   Charlie Brodie   128
Positive Visibility   Aidan Summers   129
Queer Magic   Theo Parish   130
Not Quite Yet   Chloe Smith   132

How To Be You   135

Self-Portrait with an iPhone   Dean Atta   137
The World Well Lost IV   Marc-André Raffalovich   139
working out – maybe 2 days a week   Charlie Castelletti   140
The Law Concerning Mermaids   Kei Miller   142
Affirmations for Bisexual Humans   Charlotte Moore   143
How to Dance with Hoverflies   Jack Cooper   144
Practice   Mary Jean Chan   145
once a marine biologist told me
     octopuses have three hearts   Denice Frohman   146
First Time Sexting   Andrew McMillan   148
They   Raquel Salas Rivera   150
A Gay Poem   Keith Jarrett   151
from A Queerification   Regie Cabico   154
non-binary completionist   Aaron Cawood   155
Criss-Cross   Charlie Castelletti   156

Advice   159

Tips to Begin With   David Ly   161
To the Young Person . . .   Peter Scalpello   162
What I Always Wanted Poetry
     to Tell Me   Elizabeth Gibson   163
To a Son Growing Up   Robert Hamberger   164
dear friend   Ryan Douglass   165
The Hopes   Colette Bryce   167
The Unknown   Alex Thornber   168
As Much As You Can   C. P. Cavafy   171

A Time to Live	Anna de Noailles	172
How to Come Out as Gay	Dean Atta	174
I think you can take a break from working on yourself	Charlotte Moore	177
Survival Guide	Joy Ladin	178
These Waves of Your Great Heart	Edward Carpenter	180
The Journey	Mary Oliver	183

Those Who Made Us   187

How Do I Love Thee?	Wilfred Owen	189
Shadwell Stair	Wilfred Owen	190
My Sad Captains	Thom Gunn	191
Who Ever Loved That Loved Not at First Sight?	Christopher Marlowe	192
The Foreboding	Robert Graves	193
Absence	Charlotte Mew	194
Funeral Blues	W. H. Auden	195
One Year After	Claude McKay	196
A Girl	Michael Field	198
Speculation	Radclyffe Hall	199
We Two	Radclyffe Hall	200
Tired	Langston Hughes	201
The Way That Lovers Use	Rupert Brooke	202
from The Last Meeting	Siegfried Sassoon	203
Two Loves	Lord Alfred Douglas	205
Apologia	Oscar Wilde	208
We Are Librarian	So Mayer	210

The Road from Hebden Bridge   Elizabeth Gibson   212

Who Are We Now and Where Will We Be?   215

Briefly, there were books   Jessica Verdi   217
Not Even   Ocean Vuong   220
Over the Great City   Edward Carpenter   226
Erased   Sasha Torchinsky   227
Open   Dale Booton   228
I Am the Mob   John McCullough   229
Here Be   Harry Josephine Giles   230
Pride   Travis Alabanza   231
Thoughts on Romance as
    the Heat Index Rises   Kayleb Rae Candrilli   233
i love you to the moon &   Chen Chen   234
Us   Nikita Gill   235
What Kind of Times Are These   Adrienne Rich   236
By Heart   Carol Ann Duffy   237
Future   Nicoletta Poungias   238
O Me! O Life!   Walt Whitman   239
Steps   Charlie Castelletti   240
Now, always, more   Grace Copeland-Tucker   244
Fragment 60   Sappho   246

Index of First Lines   249
Index of Poets and Translators   257
Copyright Acknowledgements   263
Compiler Acknowledgements   269

Introduction

There is no one way to introduce an anthology of queer poetry, just as there is no one way to be queer. But there are simply so few queer-specific poetry anthologies out there in the world. What *He, She, They, Us* offers is an exciting and eclectic introduction into queer poetry both old and new, from well-known writers to newly discovered voices. It is an anthology for any queer person to read at any point in their journey, taking us through some of the experiences that shape us into who we are today. It is an inclusive collection that is welcoming of everyone, showcasing a set of universal experiences that we can all identify with. From crushes, to exciting ventures, to that feeling of not ever being good enough for the world – I hope this book provides whatever it is you need from it: whether it be an antidote or relief from current stresses, an exercise in visibility, or a joyous way to pass the time. It has certainly been a joy collecting these poems for you.

When I first started compiling this anthology, it was a combination of returning to my favourite poems, scouring the internet for new voices, and approaching writers I adore and requesting they feature in this work. It is very much a labour of love, from me to you. But there were, of course, a few names I knew I would turn to: Thom Gunn, Wilfred Owen, Robert Graves, Charlotte Mew, Oscar Wilde, W. H. Auden – so many poets I first discovered as a child and whose words cemented themselves into my consciousness; whether or not I knew of their queerness at the time is, in some ways, irrelevant – they speak a universal language that anyone, no matter how they identify, can understand. But returning to them with the understanding that they might have, in one way or another, felt this very thing that I might be feeling has shifted an appreciation for their words and reshaped my understanding of a poem I once thought might have been, simply, about one kind of love. And that sits at the very heart of this collection; that there is no one way to be, to identify, to exist or to love. For me, there is power in looking at those who came before us, for wisdom and for guidance. It reminds us where we come from, of those who paved the way for us to become the 'us' we are today. That there is a history of battles won.

There is also a power that comes in reading the words being written and spoken now, with an understanding of what it means to be queer in the twenty-first century. Some poems show that there is still some way to go. Poems like 'Elegy', written by Harry Josephine Giles in the aftermath of Brianna Ghey's murder, remind us that the world can still be a hostile or even dangerous environment for some of our community. But poetry can help us to process loss and heartache, and to overcome, heal and give meaning to the pivotal moments that define our community. However, there is also so much joy to be found in the world; and the majority of this book is dedicated to celebrating us. Swathes of poems in the sections We Are Strong and Queer Joy tell the world that we are happy, we are strong – and stronger together – and will overcome any difficulties thrown our way.

So go forth, fiercely and queerly.

Charlie Castelletti, 2024

Moments

There are times in our lives that define us, that show us who we are. In this section, you will find poems that speak to those unexpected moments that set our hearts aflutter – or break them. Whether the sparky moment of first holding your crush's hand, the first time you spotted them across the football field, or the times you couldn't stop thinking about them, these poets beautifully express those feelings of hope, desire, excitement, separation and what it means to linger on moments that stay with us long after they have happened.

Episode of Hands

The unexpected interest made him flush.
Suddenly he seemed to forget the pain,—
Consented,—and held out
One finger from the others.

The gash was bleeding, and a shaft of sun
That glittered in and out among the wheels,
Fell lightly, warmly, down into the wound.

And as the fingers of the factory owner's son,
That knew a grip for books and tennis
As well as one for iron and leather,—
As his taut, spare fingers wound the gauze
Around the thick bed of the wound,
His own hands seemed to him
Like wings of butterflies
Flickering in sunlight over summer fields.

The knots and notches,—many in the wide
Deep hand that lay in his,—seemed beautiful.
They were like the marks of wild ponies' play,—
Bunches of new green breaking a hard turf.

And factory sounds and factory thoughts
Were banished from him by that larger, quieter hand
That lay in his with the sun upon it.
And as the bandage knot was tightened
The two men smiled into each other's eyes.

Hart Crane

We Two Boys together Clinging

We two boys together clinging,
One the other never leaving,
Up and down the roads going, North and South excursions
    making,
Power enjoying, elbows stretching, fingers clutching,
Arm'd and fearless, eating, drinking, sleeping, loving,
No law less than ourselves owning, sailing, soldiering, thieving,
    threatening,
Misers, menials, priests alarming, air breathing, water drinking,
    on the turf or the sea-beach dancing,
Cities wrenching, ease scorning, statutes mocking, feebleness
    chasing,
Fulfilling our foray.

Walt Whitman

A Football Player

If I could paint you, friend, as you stand there,
Guard of the goal, defensive, open-eyed,
Watching the tortured bladder slide and glide
Under the twinkling feet; arms bare, head bare,
The breeze a-tremble through crow-tufts of hair;
Red-brown in face, and ruddier having spied
A wily foeman breaking from the side,
Aware of him, – of all else unaware:
If I could limn you, as you leap and fling
Your weight against his passage, like a wall;
Clutch him and collar him, and rudely cling
For one brief moment till he falls – you fall:
My sketch would have what Art can never give,
Sinew and breath and body; it would live.

Edward Cracroft Lefroy

A Room of Firsts

No bus comes this way. No train track touches this village.
You have to get here by flooded backroads, around diversions.
Look for the window with thin violet curtains drawn at all hours.
Find a brown door on a side street, knock twice, up the stairs
across the uncarpeted landing, open the flaking white door,
and you'll find Chloe sitting on a creaking black office chair,
the yellow cushion showing through. She was the first person
I told. Beside rows of Polaroids on the wall, the first pride flag
I saw, the first time I felt the colours under my fingertips.
The first queer person I knew. The first person to say gay
and not mean filth, abomination, sin, hush. The first to say
queer and mean home, ease, bliss, laughing till you snort.
In her wardrobe mirror, fairy lights coiled round the frame,
I heard my name for the first time, I saw a full face that fit me.
I took off boyhood like a knock-off leather jacket, too tight
round my broad shoulders. I slipped my lanky, scarred body
into a peach sundress, into empire lines, mermaids' tails,
pinafores, cinched silk, halters, kaftans, lace, fit and flares.
The beaming girl in my reflection pointed at a high shelf,
the shining rows of lipstick: Bountiful Blush, Chunky Cherry,
Rose Muse, Kiss Me Coral, Dangerous Crimson, Soft Vienna.
Sitting on the edge of her New York skyline duvet, a skyscraper
underneath my stretch-marked thighs, she shows me what to do.
Smacking lips, a gentle pop. Her thumb, straightening a smudge.
The bristles of the mascara wand, Chloe's warm fingers pushing

my head side to side. Me blinking hard, the image coming clear.
The purple starry bottle of Lavender Pillow Mist from Boots
on her desk, flecks of dark roots in her ponytailed red hair.
My hands too shaky for the stubby brush, she paints me.
Smokey winged eyeliner with a touch of glitter, glinting
in the corners of my almost watering greenish hazel eyes.
Her calm breath, blowing on my candy pink nails when I tell her
who I fancied. Bradley Stannard, who sat behind me in History.
I ask her the time. Dad's coming to pick me up in an hour.
He is driving past marshland, empty harvesters, ditch bluebells.
She passes me a half-empty beige pack of sensitive makeup wipes.
Scrubbing till I'm rhubarb red, and my grey eye bags surface.
I use more than I need, ask if I got it all. I start chipping away
at my nails. I rinse the scarlet lipstick stains off my buck teeth.
Binning a mound of crumpled wipes, the smears of sparkle,
blotches of foundation and Velveteen Strawberry in my palm.

Karl Knights

Mark[1] the Second[2]

[1] Some early November mornings ago on Tinder, he on his mountain bike, I in my jogging shoes, both of us in cycling shorts and face masks, distanced by a diversion road and a police checkpoint that divide his side of the city from mine. What I remember is his smile, innocently adoring, almost goes from ear to ear. His hands, too. Dear reader, this is no scientific basis, only a lived experience, but it is possible to fall in love with a person's hands. Synecdoche, I remember from high school English, is a figure of speech. Sometimes, the body remembers the parts, not the whole. There is no undoing of it, no, none.

[2] There is no Mark the First, I have to insist. I can no longer remember his face and will not dwell on absence.

Alton Melvar M Dapanas

Romance

To clasp you now and feel your head close-pressed,
Scented and warm against my beating breast;

To whisper soft and quivering your name,
And drink the passion burning in your frame;

To lie at full length, taut, with cheek to cheek,
And tease your mouth with kisses till you speak

Love words, mad words, dream words, sweet senseless words,
Melodious like notes of mating birds;

To hear you ask if I shall love always,
And myself answer: Till the end of days;

To feel your easeful sigh of happiness
When on your trembling lips I murmur: Yes;

It is so sweet. We know it is not true.
What matters it? The night must shed her dew.

We know it is not true, but it is sweet—
The poem with this music is complete.

Claude McKay

Reminiscence

Just once we met.
It seems so long ago.
So long . . . and yet
Men would not think it so
Who count their time by years.
Just once we met . . .
And now we never meet,
Is it regret
(I lost a friend so sweet)
That stings my heart to tears?

I clasped your hand,
But scarcely said a word!
We stood as children stand
Whose souls are stirred
To great shy love they cannot comprehend.
I clasped your hand . . .
And looked into your eyes,
My spirit spanned
Your spirit's mysteries,
But feared to call you 'friend'.

Olive Custance

Demonstration

We practise anatomy
in the sweat of your single bed,
wanting to know every part of a person.

Ulna, patella, phalanges,
       frenulum, philtrum, lunula;
language so sharp I can press it in you like a pin.

Here – this here
is a place I can love.

Jack Cooper

Rain Kiss

I miss the touch of lip to lip
Resuscitation, rejuvenation, that spiritual reincarnation
Of kissing in the rain – how insane am I to miss her?
Or maybe simply craving that sensation,
The dizzy miracle of knowing someone loves you –
Or, at least, of thinking that they do.
They say it's like hypnosis when the pink psychosis
Hits you like a fresh, new drug to the lungs.
Photosynthesis from sun to skin and
When their fingers sink into you like butter –
And make your sleeping spirit flutter
Like a butterfly, pleasant as a windchime,
As a hand in mine, as a gentle breeze kisses my cheeks
Like muttering wind in country summertime.
These are all the things I felt when she was mine –
Orange, so much orange in the sky
That I could eat it, heat it, curl it up and keep it
In the space between her nose and upper lip –
Stroke it down the curve of both her hips or
Let it crackle, electric static bubble, between our fingertips.
Touching, so much touching, I could giggle
From every nervous wriggle, struggle to ever feel
We had touched enough – and so much love,
Like dripping nectarines, pomegranate seeds, so red and
Succulent, hazy and hallucinogenic, giddy and magnetic

Between my temples where the white noise finally
Fell silent. I was vibrant and alive
In everything I felt, velvet and silk, overpowering my weak
And waiting limbs . . . like tissue paper in the falling rain.
Winter is just winter nowadays. Rain is rain and
That is how the world stays: safe and empty,
Plenty to do and nothing that really matters
As the drizzle pitter-patters to the gutters of my street.
So, when the handsome princes ask to meet,
I do not go – I know they simply can't compete
With a cruel girl who'd leave me stranded,
Empty-handed, in the dark and lonely world . . .
Who has left my ragdoll heart with stains
Like black squid ink. Dark thinking, an ever-sinking sadness,
Belladonna madness, dewdrops running through my lashes,
Leaving dark rivers down my face and ocean crashes
Leave the shore then disappear without a trace . . .
Like all the love songs written gone to waste.
I know that my lips will never taste the same, and so
I choose to stay alone within the pain, and vape
The scent of cherries, sweet escape, for it's scary being alone
Without a lover, grounding all your levitating bones.
I am an illusion now, a trudging execution, and
I see so many people – meet and kiss and fall –
Like I did, once upon a time, safely in a vanilla cocoon,
Washed clean by the monsoon of all that love and beauty . . .
A hologram, entirely inside my head,

For I was just a ragdoll in a hungry woman's bed.
I notice two girls kissing, smiling, glowing in the winter rain,
Warm despite the January ice – it looks so nice and
I wonder if I'll feel that again.

Freja Nicole Woolf

A Renewal

Having used every subterfuge
To shake you, lies, fatigue, or even that of passion,
Now I see no way but a clean break.
I add that I am willing to bear the guilt.

You nod assent. Autumn turns windy, huge,
A clear vase of dry leaves vibrating on and on.
We sit, watching. When I next speak
Love buries itself in me, up to the hilt.

James Merrill

Flight

Our

hands touch

on the steps

at the side of the stage.

The   sparks like   an   uprush

of birds taking   flight.

We connect.

Two routes converge

make a pathway.

The   beginning of regrets   are   exciting

and direct.

I signal

I'm   about to take off

she signals she's prepared to

keep pace.

It's time to change

direction. We lean into the rhythm.

Find   a   bar.

Kae Tempest

On the Stairs

As I was going down those ill-famed stairs
you were coming in the door, and for a second
I saw your unfamiliar face and you saw mine.
Then I hid so you wouldn't see me again,
and you hurried past me, hiding your face,
and slipped inside the ill-famed house
where you couldn't have found pleasure any more
    than I did.

And yet the love you were looking for, I had to give you;
the love I was looking for—so your tired,
knowing eyes implied—
you had to give me.
Our bodies sensed and sought each other;
our blood and skin understood.

But we both hid ourselves, flustered.

C. P. Cavafy,
translated by Edmund Keeley and Philip Sherrard

Glimpse

on the pitch by my house   the weekly game
of football   there was one lad   already
famous in our class for having snogged a girl
and still my friend   despite the pull
of the pack mentality I always felt
outside of   I had no skill   could only
put my body in front of someone else
in hopes of slowing them for a moment
and this time it caused my friend to fall
and   in the split second it took for him
to regain himself   I saw   slipped
from shorts and briefs   his whole private self
though he hadn't noticed   still giggling
at my sudden prowess at defence
and after that   there were other times   crowding
into a friend's bedroom   me pretending
not to look as someone showed himself
to a girl   and the emptiness that followed
nobody yet ready to do the things
that come after   though it was still deliberate
and so different from that earlier time
the grass   that glimpse of something that seemed

to be all potential   tiny sapling
not yet seeding   just another part
of our innocence   fear and lust and shame
not yet ripened to full blush

Andrew McMillan

Invisible Boy

1.
When Sheila flicked up the hood of her cloak
the sound it made was queer
the cry of an alien bird.
I picture blue-grey landscapes, the bird felled.
Falling. It was the sound of wind
through trees above an empty football field.
A circle of boys forming like a bad spell
casting out another.

2.
In Dungeons & Dragons Sheila plays
the role of Thief, though
I'm not sure what she stole. I stole
glimpses of my friends as they changed
for PE. I stole memories of their shaved necks
smelling of hormones and Lynx.
When I came out to my father he said
You've robbed us of grandchildren.
Call me the thief of potential futures.

3.
This is me writing about myself
through Sheila, who could turn invisible
when she raised the hood of her cloak.
Her invisibility was a gift.
Mine was thrust on me by legislation
Section 28, a nameless
strangulation permeating the air
the way those in a house with a gas leak
have no idea that they're dying.

4.
Remind me how it goes. Be gay but don't
rub it in my face. Your face plays
no part in my gayness – see how I shrink
and expand for you, deepening my voice.
Walking past gangs of boys at school
I'd hold my breath, pretend I was invisible
any minute expecting them to shriek.
Each boy became the head of a hydra.

5.

In primary school other boys dressed as policemen,
firemen, cowboys. I pulled a blue
silk dress from the costume box, swished it
about my shoulders like a cloak
like a magician about to perform his trick
here I go, get ready, you won't see me.
You won't see me.

6.

You know I'm scared of being alone
Sheila says, and I carry this same fear.
Once family have fallen away, what comes
to even the balance?

7.

In the final episode of Dungeons & Dragons
Sheila chooses to give up her gift.
I still have mine. We adapt to survive.
Now when I pass by drunken lads
I stiffen my spine, stick out my chin.
I flick the hood of my coat up.

Matthew Haigh

The Trick

Once, sparks really did ignite from my lips after i kissed him
He said it was only a trick of the light
A seaweed-scented sunset

When you kissed me, my lips ignited once more
Sparks flashed into bluebirds and i grabbed one
You grinned, saying to hold our songs softly
But i said we'd only work if i hold our magic tightly to my chest

You whispered you knew a trick on how to love and be free
Gently kissed my fist open
Promised the bluebird would fly back to us

David Ly

Natural Habitat

It arrives in the kitchen
one palm braced over the metal lid
of a French press, the smell of coffee blank & demanding:

my high school love, nudging me
aside, and insisting we set the timer for three minutes exactly.
no milk. no sugar. only the black soil between our teeth.

I mix cream cheese into my scrambled eggs
& my mom asks if it reminds me of them.
I half forget about the way these
old & grateful habits still live in my body,
casual reminders of past lives, a historic fondness
that keeps the eggs from burning.

I scrape skin off the pan & drift while
the timer counts back from three minutes,
knowing we didn't break up but blinked out,
died in each other's arms,
awoke in mismatched resurrection & both felt abandoned

it's an honor that all these years later we still conjure
the most affectionate bitterness
in one another

the timer beeps and I uncurl ribbons into my mug,
watch the steam wind back into itself.
I lean into the granite cabinet
& look out the fog-wet window
& breathe,
again & again,
into this
new and dying body

Kelsey Day

Scenes

The poems in this section hover over the time and space of specific places: at the poolside, in a cafe, bar or gallery; in your home, alone or with everyone around you. There are all kinds of places available to us; some that make us feel seen and provide a refuge; some that entrap us, expose us, places we'll never forget. The important thing is that we take up these spaces. Because we belong there.

The Gallery Floor

On days when we'd go to the galleries,
I chose my shoes based on their sound
against the concrete or hardwood floors.
Elegant but hushed, I wanted the day's rhythm
punctuated by our companionate shuffle,
overlaid by the chatter of the patrons
and our cheeky side remarks. Spoken
in low tones during the intersection
of our orbits, we'd reveal which pictures
we would hang in our homes,
ones that left us besotted, and those
we just couldn't care less about—
a statement typically followed by a nod
and an exit into the next exhibition room.
We'd spend time together elsewhere too
but, in the galleries, our edges became soft—
a lifting only possible with proximity,
like birds finding the upwash,
my feet barely brushing the floor.

Erica Gillingham

To Lallie

(Outside the British Museum).

Up those Museum steps you came,
And straightway all my blood was flame,
    O Lallie, Lallie!

The world (I had been feeling low)
In one short moment's space did grow
    A happy valley.

There was a friend, my friend, with you;
A meagre dame in peacock blue
    Apparelled quaintly:

This poet-heart went pit-a-pat;
I bowed and smiled and raised my hat;
    You nodded—faintly.

My heart was full as full could be;
You had not got a word for me,
    Not one short greeting;

That nonchalant small nod you gave
(The tyrant's motion to the slave)
    Sole mark'd our meeting.

Is it so long? Do you forget
That first and last time that we met?
    The time was summer;

The trees were green; the sky was blue;
Our host presented me to you—
    A tardy comer.

You look'd demure, but when you spoke
You made a little, funny joke,
    Yet half pathetic.

Your gown was grey, I recollect,
I think you patronized the sect
    They call "aesthetic."

I brought you strawberries and cream,
And plied you long about a stream
    With duckweed laden;

We solemnly discussed the—heat.
I found you shy and very sweet,
    A rosebud maiden.

Ah me, to-day! You passed inside
To where the marble gods abide:
    Hermes, Apollo,

Sweet Aphrodite, Pan; and where,
For aye reclined, a headless fair
　　Beats all fairs hollow.

And I, I went upon my way,
Well—rather sadder, let us say;
　　The world looked flatter.

I had been sad enough before,
A little less, a little more,
　　What *does* it matter?

Amy Levy

A Wall Flower

I lounge in the doorway and languish in vain
While Tom, Dick and Harry are dancing with Jane

My spirit rises to the music's beat;
There is a leaden fiend lurks in my feet!
To move unto your motion, Love, were sweet.

Somewhere, I think, some other where, not here,
In other ages, on another sphere,
I danced with you, and you with me, my dear.

In perfect motion did our bodies sway,
To perfect music that was heard alway;
Woe's me, that am so dull of foot to-day!

To move unto your motion, Love, were sweet;
My spirit rises to the music's beat—
But, ah, the leaden demon in my feet!

Amy Levy

Skin Tags

I tell my hands to loosen
my tie, unbutton
my shirt, fasten
tight goggles and cap
to my skull. Begin limping
towards feet scraping dirty tiles,
the smell of chlorine,
the shoulder-blades of boys
diving. I tell my hands to ignore
the skin-tags on my neck and hips,
instead cover the purple marks
etched all over my back, calves,
autographs of the first man to touch
me like my skin was his own.

Karl Knights

Things That Are Rare

It is so easy to imagine your absence.
Maybe it is night, we are still handsome.
All the young are.
It is so easy. Another thing to be beautiful.
How gently the curtain falls back down
and the room is dark again, the season
of in-betweenities,
my eyes heavy, my lips numb.
Fingerprints on the unjacketed books.
Inside the collars
of the shirts in the open closet –
An affluent night.
You've touched everything in my small room

Richie Hofmann

Boys in Moonlight Shine

Boys in moonlight shine
as if some distant
planet were on fire
for their benefit,

set alight by one
with fingers to burn.
They entice the night
away from mirrors

reserved for themselves
and vandalise glass
as a star would drop
into a sea of milk.

Gregory Woods

After Sunday Lunch

After Sunday lunch
the breaking voices
of a solitary world
close family doors

behind them and go
kicking cans to blazes.
Their paths intersect
but they never meet.

They can hear each other
keen in the empty
streets, adam's apples
reckless with restraint.

Gregory Woods

Jesus at the Gay Bar

He's here in the midst of it –
right at the centre of the dance floor,
robes hitched up to His knees
to make it easy to spin.

At some point in the evening
a boy will touch the hem of His robe
and beg to be healed, beg to be
anything other than this;

and He will reach His arms out,
sweat-damp, and weary from dance.
He'll cup this boy's face in His hand
and say,

my beautiful child
there is nothing in this heart of yours
that ever needs to be healed.

Jay Hulme

Can a thunderstorm happen in mid-winter . . .

For Maria Maksakova

Can a thunderstorm happen in mid-winter
And a sky blue as indigo?
I love that your eyes are crossed
And that your soul has a crossing.

And I like those shivery shoulders,
The quickness of your sprightly gait,
Your empty and frugal speech,
Your mermaid-tight thighs.

I like that in your chill
I am, as in high fire, smelting,
I like that – can I admit it! –
I like that I don't appeal to you.

Sophia Parnok
Translated by Rainie Oet

On the Road to the Sea

We passed each other, turned and stopped for half an hour, then
  went our way,
     I who make other women smile did not make you—
But no man can move mountains in a day.
     So this hard thing is yet to do.

But first I want your life:—before I die I want to see
     The world that lies behind the strangeness of your eyes,
There is nothing gay or green there for my gathering, it may be,
     Yet on brown fields there lies
A haunting purple bloom: is there not something in grey skies
     And in grey sea?
     I want what world there is behind your eyes,
     I want your life and you will not give it me.

     Now, if I look, I see you walking down the years,
     Young, and through August fields—a face, a thought, a
swinging dream
         perched on a stile—;
     I would have liked (so vile we are!) to have taught you
tears
     But most to have made you smile.

To-day is not enough or yesterday: God sees it all—
Your length on sunny lawns, the wakeful rainy nights—; tell me—;
         (how vain to ask), but it is not a question—just a call—;
Show me then, only your notched inches climbing up the garden
    wall,
         I like you best when you are small.

         Is this a stupid thing to say
              Not having spent with you one day?
         No matter; I shall never touch your hair
         Or hear the little tick behind your breast,
              And as a flying bird
         Brushes the branches where it may not rest
         I have brushed your hand and heard
         The child in you: I like that best
So small, so dark, so sweet; and were you also then too grave and
    wise?
         Always I think. Then put your far off little hand in mine;—
              Oh! let it rest;
I will not stare into the early world beyond the opening eyes,
         Or vex or scare what I love best.
         But I want your life before mine bleeds away—
              Here—not in heavenly hereafters—soon,—
              I want your smile this very afternoon,
         (The last of all my vices, pleasant people used to say,
              I wanted and I sometimes got—the Moon!)

You know, at dusk, the last bird's cry,
  And round the house the flap of the bat's low flight,
    Trees that go black against the sky
And then—how soon the night!

  No shadow of you on any bright road again,
And at the darkening end of this—what voice? whose kiss? As if
  you'd say!
It is not I who have walked with you, it will not be I who take away
    Peace, peace, my little handful of the gleaner's grain
    From your reaped fields at the shut of day.

  Peace! Would you not rather die
    Reeling,—with all the cannons at your ear?
  So, at least, would I,
    And I may not be here
    To-night, to-morrow morning or next year.
    Still I will let you keep your life a little while,
      See dear?

  I have made you smile.

Charlotte Mew

Girl Guides

we met on a Girl Guides trip (she texted first)
which caused me to check my phone
in French class at school, a different school
to the one she was at which had a pool
but wasn't private she told me
to focus on the sound of leaves
crunching under my shoes whenever
I felt sad and that the dress code for
her fourteenth birthday party was red
which meant I expected her to invite me
so when she posted photos of herself
and her friends with Smirnoff Ice on MySpace
that night I hid my red turtleneck jumper
down the side of my bed and dreamt
about her saying sorry and kissing me
in a way which made me wake up
shocked to see that she had texted to say
my friend told me you like me, is it true?

Jo Morris Dixon

To the Girl at the Bus Stop

They say I'm not supposed to love you.
I say then why does it feel like the solar system
has parted to help you walk towards me?
I say the universe built me this life
so I could find you right here,
standing at this bus stop
with your black bag
with lime-green edges,
waiting for the same bus
at eight every morning.
I say don't tell me
love doesn't look like this:
all peach summer dresses and warm hands,
a smile like a secret caught between your teeth.

Nikita Gill

Words and Music

She moves about in the tiny flat
with the long strides of a goddess,
fixing this, or watering that,
mixing the books up, wearing my shirt.

She dials the little radio
through crashing waves of static,
through 'words, words, words!'
and finds a hidden symphony

then moves a chair to occupy
the single square of morning sun,
basks in the full length of herself,
ankles hooked on the window sill,

feet conducting sky. She asks me
if I love her. I wouldn't quite
go that far. It's just that
if she leaves me, I'm done for.

Colette Bryce

Queer

How old was I? Thirteen maybe.
One insult too many smashed that armour
I'd constructed: 'Fucking queer.'
This classmate looked inside me,
knew the secret, smelt it. What made him see?
Me fancying men, other boys. Watching their
legs inside jeans, their chests under
buttoned shirts, a throat or a knee.
I sniffed it with him:
disgust; difference; always outside; never let in
to marriage, kids, happiness. Locked in that bathroom
for an hour thinking: *Take it away. I'll pull off my skin,*
stop my eyes, do anything. I'm not one of them.
How long does it take to own yourself? How long has it been?

Robert Hamberger

We Are Strong

Being queer is joyous. But it can also, at times, bring with it certain difficulties. Navigating these aspects of our identity amongst the prejudices of the world is something we all, in our own way, face. The poems in this section demonstrate that whatever we go through as an individual or as a community, there is a large collection of wonderfully, beautifully diverse people to prop us up when things get hard. We are fearless and strong. We triumph through conflict. We come together and survive.

Dysphoria

It's true that I'm im-
patient under affliction. So?
Most of what the dead can

do is difficult to carry. As for
gender I can't explain it
any more than a poem: there

was an instinct, I followed
it. A song. A bell. I saw
deer tracks in the snow. Little

split hearts beckoned me
across the lawn. My body
bucked me, fond of me.

Here is how you bear this flourish.
Bud, I'm buckling to blossoms now.

Oliver Baez Bendorf

The Ride That Loops Infinitely/ Tall Bed Above Water

I wasn't born in a girl's body. But there are certain tracks

I make in Coaster Boss

that loop infinitely

in a way the game can't account for.

Like this suspended coaster I just made that never

lets its riders out.

Because I want an audience

to put on Junie's red sweater and

dance in front of, bottomless.

An impossibly steep hill, and only one car,

which slides back down

and is launched up, again and again,

until even the girl Guests stop screaming and put

their hands down.

There has to only be one car because—I just learned this the

hard way—

if there are two, they'll crash into each other,

one going up, one coming down—

death and flying heads and hands on fire.

It's the same with me. I can only be one car

on my track—and I have to "suspend" all disbelief

to dream about being called Junie,

hands on my heart in my bedroom in the dark.

Trying to make no sound at all, trying

to even stop breathing.

*

(I watch my shadow on the wall. Myself and my shadow—
soul twins.)

Rainie Oet

#131 Lapras

"People have driven Lapras almost to the point of extinction. In the evenings, this Pokémon is said to sing plaintively as it seeks what few others of its kind still remain." – Pokémon Emerald

My ___ corseted in whirlpool & whalebone. My ___ all carapace & no blubber. My ___ swims without schools. My ___ is a lone American WWII bomber returning to base. My ___ freckled with bullet holes. My ___ shrapnel. My ___ mistaken as symbol of resilience. My ___ mistakes anchor for torpedo. My ___ a mistake. My ___ at stake. My ___ as image of survival. My ___ on pedestal. My ___ plural. My ___ not buoy. My ___ not brave. My ___ is not a ___. My ___ numbered. My ___ sings the language of boats. My ___ sometimes forgets how to breathe above water. My ___ is both hovercraft & harpoon, both failure & possibility. My ___ breaking surface. My ___ is war cry & swan song. My ___ is a fossil from the future. Look at my <u>body</u>. How big, how blue, how beautiful.

Winter Chen

Reconciliation

Waiting by his side, drenching
pupils, I imagined how his lips
taste of lemon curd, bright like
brass, flames of my youth on his
skin. How I wished for our knees
to brush, to grab his arm, softest
ball of yarn unwrapping, running.
No more whispers, we are trumpets
heralding that we have not sinned.
Yet I would go down to hell to reheat
his pizza if he asked me to. Father,
the lakes do freeze, it starts to snow
now, it's been so long since my last
confession. I have him buried in my
chest and I still want him to be mine.

Luís Costa

The Moon is Trans

The moon is trans.

From this moment forward, the moon is trans.

You don't get to write about the moon anymore unless you respect
  that.

You don't get to talk to the moon anymore unless you use her
  correct pronouns.

You don't get to send men to the moon anymore unless their job is

to bow down before her and apologize for the sins of the earth.

She is waiting for you, pulling at you softly,

telling you to shut the fuck up already please.

Scientists theorize the moon was once a part of the earth

that broke off when another planet struck it.

Eve came from Adam's rib.

Etc.

Do you believe in the power of not listening

to the inside of your own head?

I believe in the power of you not listening

to the inside of your own head.

This is all upside down.

We should be talking about the ways that blood

is similar to the part of outer space between the earth and the moon

but we're busy drawing it instead.

The moon is often described as dead, though she is very much alive.

The moon has not known the feeling of not wanting to be dead

for any extended period of time

in all of her existence, but

she is not delicate and she is not weak.

She is constantly moving away from you the only way she can.

She never turns her face from you because of what you might do.

She will outlive everything you know.

Joshua Jennifer Espinoza

All the Dead Boys Look Like Me

Last time I saw myself die is when police killed Jessie Hernandez

A 17 year old brown queer // who was
sleeping in their car

Yesterday I saw myself die again // Fifty times I died in Orlando // &

I remember reading // Dr. José Esteban Muñoz
before he passed

I was studying at NYU // where he was teaching // where he wrote shit

That made me feel like a queer brown survival was
possible // But he didn't

Survive & now // on the dancefloor // in the restroom // on the
news // in my chest

There are another fifty bodies that look like mine // & are

Dead // & I've been marching for Black Lives & talking about
police brutality

Against Native communities too // for years now // but
this morning

I feel it // I really feel it again // How can we imagine ourselves //
   We being black native

            Today // Brown people // How can we imagine
                  ourselves

When All the Dead Boys Look Like Us? // Once I asked my
   nephew where he wanted

            To go to College // What career he would like // as if

The whole world was his for the choosing // Once he answered
   me without fearing

            Tombstones or cages or the hands from a father //
               The hands of my lover

Yesterday praised my whole body // Made angels from my lips //
   Ave Maria

            Full of Grace // He propped me up like the roof of a
               cathedral // in NYC

Before we opened the news & read // & read about people who
   think two brown queers

Can't build cathedrals // only cemeteries // & each
time we kiss

A funeral plot opens // In the bedroom I accept his kiss // & I lose
my reflection

I'm tired of writing this poem // but I want to say
one last word about

Yesterday // my father called // I heard him cry for only the second
time in my life

He sounded like he loved me // it's something I'm
rarely able to hear

& I hope // if anything // his sound is what my body remembers first.

Christopher Soto

A Shropshire Lad

The street sounds to the soldiers' tread,
And out we troop to see:
A single redcoat turns his head,
He turns and looks at me.

My man, from sky to sky's so far,
We never crossed before;
Such leagues apart the world's ends are,
We're like to meet no more;

What thoughts at heart have you and I
We cannot stop to tell;
But dead or living, drunk or dry,
Soldier, I wish you well.

A. E. Housman

Eating Slurs for Breakfast

Your laugh eats up the slurs your dad scattered on your floor. You play Mariah when the worst news comes and you send me curated TikToks when the hole deepens and your vegan leather shoes threaten to stumble in. My face is the tragedy to your comedy, tears crashing in a hit and run every time I stub my toe, get dumped after the second date or am haunted by my own ghosting. You crack joke after joke, sunny side up, orange eggs in a black pan. I see lives cut short for a breakfast, you see nourishment, calories, something that will help us grow. It can't all be doom and gloom you say when we can't afford anything but our love for each other, and as you lay a grubby handprint on my white shirt, finally I laugh.

Elspeth Wilson

All Trains Are Going Local

Slowing down your body enough to feel.

Thought you were at a standstill
but you were only slowing down enough

to feel the pain. There are worse things

than running to catch the train, twisting
your ankle, the afternoon fucked.

Running to get to or away from?

the stranger who helps you up
wants to know, you who are so used to

anything scribbled on a prescription blank.

Just want the pain to go away, you say,
surprised to find yourself

reaching for someone else's hand.

Timothy Liu

Today I Love Being Alive

I wake up and eat a banana.
Stand naked in my kitchen.
Shave and listen to Billie Holiday.

My god, I'm so obsessed with you.
You're new. You're tall. You make me feel
like never putting clothes on.

Who's to say if you'll still be around
when anyone's reading this poem.
Or if the Earth will continue

(it's getting very hot!)
or if we'll get it right in language
exactly how we feel about each other.

I don't care about being remembered.
I care about a great glass of wine.
Strong men. Beautiful sentences. Italian leather.

Call me old-fashioned, really.
But when I cut myself shaving above the lip,
I lick up the blood. I don't wince.

Alex Dimitrov

Elegy

i.m. Brianna Ghey 2006–2023

Sister, you are smiling when I meet you,
half a bar of chocolate held between
your thumb and half-raised middle finger, so
at first I think you're offering the camera
a grain of fuck off magic with your grin.
But no, the eager sun is only melting
a lick of sugar down your wrist. The grass
is only watered. Your brows are only plucked.

Sister, I meant to meet you in the pit
of punks, girls to the front. I meant to brace
my marching voice on yours, our shivered longing
hoarse as rafters. I meant a moonstruck dress
my bones outgrew to settle on your shoulders.
I meant to sleep. I meant only to stay
safe in distant sisterhood. Now
it's already morning and the dogs of news

are rattling the gate before your blood
has sunk into the earth. The fife and drum.
The column's inch. The typing has begun.
My sister, when I call to pass the dead
weight from my heart to hers, says, "The worst
is hoping to hear that it wasn't . . ." But when my sisters
walk with ghosts on either side, what odds
does it make: chance or choice, the edge of hatred

finds its mark. Sister, you were born
after I first ringed my eyes with black,
after I first skinned the street and tasted
desperation, after womanhood
began to ring her furious alarms
beyond my reach. I wrote a bloody book
before you took a breath. The space you left
cannot be filled, though we, your hungered sisters,

will drown the world-tree with grief. How dare a death
be made to mean more than its cut to meaning?
How dare a poem be? Am I no different
from the coursers ripping at your years?
I turn to words to turn your loss to less
than unspeakable. I too have my devices.
Sister, you are far from the first sister
I've had to make a way to grieve – familiar

sorrows sing familiar staves – but you
deserve far better than the anaesthesia
binding my limbs, than vigils, than editing.
Sister, I am sorry. Sister, the spells
you taught yourself to shape yourself anew
could level kingdoms, but all I wish for you
is life. Here, this is my small flame.
Sister, I will always carry your name.

Harry Josephine Giles

Don't Die

I say it so often it's embedded in my skin.
            don't die
Have another cup of tea.
Did you buy the new shoes?
What's your plan for tomorrow?
                don't die,
                        don't die,
                                don't die

When the plague is over, we'll go dancing;
I hate dancing, but we'll go.
                        don't die
We'll visit that coffee shop, if it's still open;
that one you took me to, before all of this.
            don't die

What's on telly?
            don't die
What're you eating?
                don't die
What do you want from this stunted existence?
        please   don't die

I'm reaching out again,
trying to find the edges of you in the ether.
A hundred miles away, and still beside me.

Let me tell you about the future.

>   *don't die*

What we're going to do together.

>   *don't die*

The supermarket is closing soon,
you have to go and buy groceries.
Be careful, I say.

>   *Stay safe,* I say.

>   *don't die*

I say.

>   *don't die*

                    Jay Hulme

If I could pray the gay away

. . . I would not . . .

I would pray to stay this way forever. I would.

Andrés N. Ordorica

"Hope" is the thing with feathers

"Hope" is the thing with feathers –
That perches in the soul –
And sings the tune without the words –
And never stops – at all –

And sweetest – in the Gale – is heard –
And sore must be the storm –
That could abash the little Bird
That kept so many warm –

I've heard it in the chillest land –
And on the strangest Sea –
Yet – never – in Extremity,
It asked a crumb – of Me.

Emily Dickinson

A Litany for Survival

For those of us who live at the shoreline
standing upon the constant edges of decision
crucial and alone
for those of us who cannot indulge
the passing dreams of choice
who love in doorways coming and going
in the hours between dawns
looking inward and outward
at once before and after
seeking a now that can breed
futures
like bread in our children's mouths
so their dreams will not reflect
the death of ours;

For those of us
who were imprinted with fear
like a faint line in the center of our foreheads
learning to be afraid with our mother's milk
for by this weapon
this illusion of some safety to be found
the heavy-footed hoped to silence us
For all of us
this instant and this triumph
We were never meant to survive.

And when the sun rises we are afraid
it might not remain
when the sun sets we are afraid
it might not rise in the morning
when our stomachs are full we are afraid
of indigestion
when our stomachs are empty we are afraid
we may never eat again
when we are loved we are afraid
love will vanish
when we are alone we are afraid
love will never return
and when we speak we are afraid
our words will not be heard
nor welcomed
but when we are silent
we are still afraid

So it is better to speak
remembering
we were never meant to survive.

Audre Lorde

Queer Joy

These poems are here to energize us, to showcase the pride and joy of living freely as ourselves. From innocent schooldays and childhood games to sipping at an iced latte with our best friends, looking up at the night sky, or bunking off work to see that special person; we are all deserving of peace, happiness, pleasure and love.

Rainbow Road

If I could smile   like Peach then they'd call me   Daisy and keep me
in a room   filled with stuffed old animals   but the room's too hot
and   someone's left birthday cake in the animals' furry heads
and the cake's melted,   melted inside them, inside   their stuffing
brains and . . .

I   want to be hugged until   I see rainbows. I want to   play the
Rainbow Road level
    of Mario Kart and not fall off the edge. I want to   be in a dress.
I want to
    be naked in a room of naked   friends with trees growing out
of the floorboards, except
    my natural naked body is   a pink dress and no parts   and I
actually can't get
    more naked than that.

But everybody else is just watching   me turn on and off my
controller. It's charging,
out of batteries   and keeps moving me to the right,   even when
I'm not pressing
    right, so that I have to hold   the tiny thumb stick left, just to
break even, just to not move
    at all.

Rainie Oet

In Sims, I Woohoo with a Girl

The green diamond floats above
your head, your very own bar sign,
an invitation
to Express Affection and
Touch Fondly and maybe even
Express Undying
Love For on our second
date. You
bring the experience and I bring the
giant vibrating bed with the love-
heart and a fun rating of
ten. Your aspiration is to Woohoo
with fifteen sims and I am a
willing lump
under purple sheets.
Fireworks explode as my
hands touch the
mouse, click
again
     again
         again

Elspeth Wilson

playtime

there were good days / during the holidays / when your mum made us / vegetarian pasta bakes / with salad from a plastic packet / which she trusted us / to wash and let us / choose any film we wanted / so we watched things / to make us feel older / than we actually were at ten / and because I always wore shorts and a t-shirt / you told me I could play Leonardo DiCaprio / which made us excited to try things / like me drawing you / that summer we learnt / that we had parts like boys / which felt good too / and that these were too special / to be graffitied on desks

Jo Morris Dixon

school bell ring

song of daybreak on the playground
toothy grins flash over the astro turf and
knee-high socked legs
make their way towards each other
dimples ghost across smooth cheeks
the day has begun
now that I have seen you

school bell ring

song of freedom
ring around the Rosie
giggles floating in the air
but we laugh only for each other
how lovely it is
to have a friend like you

school bell ring

song of return
when teacher speaks,
I dream
me and you on the swings
what great heights
can we go that high again?

school bell ring

song of twilight
side by side we walk
sweet silence before the end
I look to you
You look to me
the promise of tomorrow

Hope Ndaba

Iced Coffee

TURNING TO A FRIEND AND AGREEING THAT THERE'S SOMETHING REALLY QUEER ABOUT ICED COFFEE, ISN'T REALLY ABOUT ICED COFFEE AT ALL. IT'S ABOUT FEELING AT HOME. IT'S FINDING PIECES OF OURSELVES IN SILLY THINGS BECAUSE FOR SO LONG, WE DIDN'T EVEN GET SILLY THINGS. AND, THAT'S THE *THING* THAT STRUCK ME MOST ABOUT BISEXUAL CULTURE. WE'RE ALWAYS STRADDLING TWO WORLDS. AND, FOR MOST, WE HAVE TO MAKE OUR OWN HOME, IN BETWEEN. PREFERABLY, A HOME, WITH ICED COFFEE

Charlotte Moore

Ringing in Sick to go Mermaid Hunting

Once when I wasn't, I rang in sick for the evening shift
and went instead to meet you at Raftery's in Kilcolgan,
we left your car there and I drove south-west down
the summer solstice evening, hitting for the coast
we squinted through sunglasses at Ballinderreen and Kinvara
but didn't stop, turned for Fanore at Ballyvaughan,
you leaning back feet on the dash singing along
to the Indigo Girls and Johnny Cash, and asking me
where we were headed, but messing about,
I wouldn't say, I told you on a day like this, trust me
it will all work out: we're going mermaid hunting
and the signs are good for catching.

There were no mermaids though, at the pier before Black head
just one dolphin doing her bit for inter-speciel integration
she came in waist-deep to meet us and we were drenched,
and charmed. From behind wet hair you asked me how
I'd known and in my stupid humour I said oh you know

I had my people call her people, that's how it goes,
this event was arranged for your pleasure dear,
so of course pushed me backwards off the pier
then jumped yourself and our dolphin circled
as if she got the joke, spearing herself four feet
skywards above our heads then vanishing beneath.

You pushed me backwards off the pier and then jumped.
Us two fools, we swam through seaweed,
feeling elemental, you're half fish you said,
yea but I've caught you this time.

In Lenane's at dusk we had chowder, and a pint, I sat
with salty skin and hair and when you joined
the jobs-worth band to sing 'The Dimming of the Day' for me,
you made every hair on every sunburned neck there stand.
You slept then as I drove but I woke you in Kilcolgan to send you
down the Craughwell road, me? I hit for home, but parked
instead at Whitestrand beach, on the longest evening of the year
too full of everything to go inside just then.

Sarah Clancy

Having a Coke with You

is even more fun than going to San Sebastian, Irún, Hendaye,
 Biarritz, Bayonne
or being sick to my stomach on the Travesera de Gracia in Barcelona
partly because in your orange shirt you look like a better happier
 St. Sebastian
partly because of my love for you, partly because of your love for
 yoghurt
partly because of the fluorescent orange tulips around the birches
partly because of the secrecy our smiles take on before people and
 statuary
it is hard to believe when I'm with you that there can be anything
 as still
as solemn as unpleasantly definitive as statuary when right in front
 of it
in the warm New York 4 o'clock light we are drifting back and forth
between each other like a tree breathing through its spectacles

and the portrait show seems to have no faces in it at all, just paint
you suddenly wonder why in the world anyone ever did them
I look
at you and I would rather look at you than all the portraits in the
 world
except possibly for the *Polish Rider* occasionally and anyway it's in
 the Frick

which thank heavens you haven't gone to yet so we can go
    together for the first time
and the fact that you move so beautifully more or less takes care of
    Futurism
just as at home I never think of the *Nude Descending a Staircase* or
at a rehearsal a single drawing of Leonardo or Michelangelo that
    used to wow me
and what good does all the research of the Impressionists do them
when they never got the right person to stand near the tree when
    the sun sank
or for that matter Marino Marini when he didn't pick the rider as
    carefully
as the horse
            it seems they were all cheated of some marvelous
    experience
which is not going to go wasted on me which is why I'm telling you
    about it

Frank O'Hara

Immanence

A raspberry one with moist frosting, or
a lemon one with white chocolate shavings?
A door chime signals us. A donut for two in
a café with notions on a sleepy Lisburn Rd.
The low buzz chat of other people engaged
in another try. Exposed soft white light bulbs
make everything rounder. Do you see them?
Some good coffee. Two brightly green eyes.
Hammers of wet coffee grounds into the bin
remind us we're here; our treasure is delivered.
What we have been waiting for all this time.
Slowly, a dull blade halves the red-glaze donut
and it cries laughing. Blood is coming out!
You're wearing my jumper. You're eating.

Mícheál McCann

Of Course He Smells Like Lemons

His face licked by the pink of neon lights,
green marble eyes
watching our warming beers in the dark.
Under this table,
shielded from the bright stars, his leg hair
dances to Chopin
waltzes in my palm. And I want to drink
him so slowly, hard
jawlines that softly simmer in this tender
night. Four hundred
days since I imagined air around his bed,
to melt in the sheets
of merengue wrapping his thighs. Our day
will come, he tells me
I did not kiss him for the last time just yet.

Luís Costa

from The Great Lover

These I have loved:
　　　　White plates and cups, clean-gleaming,
Ringed with blue lines; and feathery, faëry dust;
Wet roofs, beneath the lamp-light; the strong crust
Of friendly bread; and many-tasting food;
Rainbows; and the blue bitter smoke of wood;
And radiant raindrops couching in cool flowers;
And flowers themselves, that sway through sunny hours,
Dreaming of moths that drink them under the moon;
Then, the cool kindliness of sheets, that soon
Smooth away trouble; and the rough male kiss
Of blankets; grainy wood; live hair that is
Shining and free; blue-massing clouds; the keen
Unpassioned beauty of a great machine;
The benison of hot water; furs to touch;
The good smell of old clothes; and other such—
The comfortable smell of friendly fingers,
Hair's fragrance, and the musty reek that lingers
About dead leaves and last year's ferns. . . .

Dear names,
And thousand other throng to me! Royal flames;
Sweet water's dimpling laugh from tap or spring;
Holes in the ground; and voices that do sing;
Voices in laughter, too; and body's pain,
Soon turned to peace; and the deep-panting train;
Firm sands; the little dulling edge of foam
That browns and dwindles as the wave goes home;
And washen stones, gay for an hour; the cold
Graveness of iron; moist black earthen mould;
Sleep; and high places; footprints in the dew;
And oaks; and brown horse-chestnuts, glossy-new;
And new-peeled sticks; and shining pools on grass;—
All these have been my loves.

Rupert Brooke

Sun catcher, record player

There's an iridescent rainbow scatter
shattered across my bedroom wall.
Sunlight reaches out its hand,
shoulder touched by disco glitter.

In chorus, queer singers sing:
You are not alone; I know a place.
The many angels, in sibling solidarity,
Rise up to catch the sun together.

We wear our hearts lit
upon our sleeves
And our music emblazoned
on our shirts
Generations of pins flagged
To our jackets.
Storied truths on our souls.

When I leave my room and listen
to the light refracted in fantasies of song
That's how it feels (silk press of bodies)
when I'm truly free to be. Me.

So spread your glass wings and fly
Soaring, joyful, in symphony.
Dancing with community, and a poem
That shines multicoloured memories.

Charlie Morris

Spout

Some months all my thoughts are one colour.
I hit a yellow mood and the world pours out its yolks:
tall stacks of *National Geographic* in Oxfam,
cranes that point uncertain fingers at the sky

while maple leaves swoop into me and cling, their veins
like roads heading everywhere in fallen, saffron cities.
Then, the teapot you saw on eBay, had to have.
It was like unpacking October and standing it on our table,

its yellow logic strict yet plump, offering an outsized handle,
a colour that might foster never-ending cups. We filled it
with boiling water, our new sun, and that first time
the copper rings around its centre made it tick-tick-tick

as if letting us know it could wipe us out if it wanted to
but we'd been spared, that we could live beside it
though should be grateful for everything of its kind
which travelled toward us, all the yellow days.

John McCullough

Sheep's Head Peninsula

As I lie on my back in the dry grass
I watch bats disturb the stars. The night
tastes of summer clams and dock leaves,
bats overhead taste flies and moths
with their snouts and wings.
I picture the word *bat* printed on a page –
it's all wrong, bat is movement, a flicker
that for a moment erases part of the night.
       So many words are wrong:
       the closed letters of *dog* – dog
       is snout and paw against my leg;
       the heaviness of *home* – home is circles
       joining. Sign was the first language:
       before blurred lips began to speak
       we opened our hands to invent
       a new world. I know this as I know night
       is better when words are erased,
       replaced by stars, and bats, and you.

Rosamund Taylor

Note: The signs described are those used in Irish Sign Language.

Mango Kiss

there were street lights
competing with stars
on the main boulevard
the night we ate mango
sticky rice, let it dissolve
in our mouths, and it was like—

    a lamp on low
    the room an amber tone
    the first time her tongue
    brushed against mine

like waking to my bed
warmed by the sun
the texture of gold-coloured yarn
fresh pies made with honey

    eaten barefoot in the kitchen
    learning to cook in a wok
    having her arms wrap
    around my waist
    as I finished the dishes

like letting a word
settle onto my taste buds
being glad that
if I could eat a colour
it would be the taste of you

Erica Gillingham

Leftovers

A jug of milk in the fridge
is what he left me;
half of his own litre
brought from town.
For the tea, we imagine, but
standing in the kitchen
brewing it strong
he feels more like ground coffee;
ember smell of him
from lighting the fire,
rough-handed from work.
Outside, rusted mountains
crease along the skyline
like his eyes, laughing now;
almost disappearing but so full,
I want to believe, of me,
and the clouds of Kerry
in that moment
they look like cream.

Eva Griffin

syntax

and if
I were to say

I love you and
I do love you

and I say it
now and again

and again
would you say

parataxis
would you see

the world revolves
anew

its axis
you

Maureen N. McLane

Something Rhymed

You're a gem, you're a holy cairn
You're a clattering shaw
You're a Tongland Bridge
You're a Solway Firth
You're a Big Water of Fleet
You're an old song, you're a valley

This feeling inside me could never deny me

You're a red deer of the forest
You're a wild goat of the moor
You're a Bladnoch malt,
A Whithorm Story, you're a friend, you're a glory.

Nothing old, nothing new, nothing ventured

Oh, you are definitely, so completely
The brightest girl of the glen.
You're a beeswing, you sing in a voice
Like a freshwater spring

Nothing older than time, nothing sweeter than wine

You are my Pinwherry,
You're my Loch Doon and Galloway,
You're my Gatehouse of Fleet,
You are philosophical, all Luce Bay,
And Whaupshill

Nothing I couldn't say.

Jackie Kay

An ode to trans bodies

Because when they told us
we'd fall in love someday,
they never meant with ourselves.

That someday
I would weep together with a trans guy onstage at a dive bar
    hugging bare chest to bare chest for the first time in public
they never told me I would buzzcut a friend's head on a Brooklyn
    fire escape,
pierce my own nose in the bathroom during COVID
or take my parents to a drag show.

I wish someone had told me
home
will become everywhere
family will become everyone
and queerness will never go extinct

I am the remnants of transcestors before me
cycling into my bones, dust to dust, ashes to ashes
and from the centrifuge I float
into the ether
the macrocosm of my own androgyne galaxy

limitless beyond my two legs
but binary bipeds
fear
the unknown.
They are scared.
They should be scared.
We are another life forward
a better life forward.

They try to stifle our love and joy
they violate and criminalize us
Commodify
Pathologize
And politicize us
But our bodies are not political

they are simply not yours.
After pride month we lower the flags
But the fags remain
I have two footlong scars, armpit to sternum and back to armpit
That signify where I end and others begin
and you may divert your eyes at the beach or swimming pool
try to push aside your discomfort

But I fought for
This life, this body,
My own internal weaponization
Pitting flesh against mind against heart
Against a world that cannot understand
Beyond the binary of self and society.

Where you see imperfection
or instability
I see resistance
Imperfect bodies are divine
Imperfect bodies are daily existence.
My body is exactly as intended
I am exactly as intended
I am transcendent
every scar, every freckle, every coarse hair

is real.

Our bodies are a record of survival
always advancing, discovering
always enough

and to be seen as we are
is to be boundless

Cal Brantley

Identity

Poetry can help us to see ourselves, to express the thoughts, feelings and anxieties we experience through the day and put to rest at night. There is no escaping who we are, and the poems in this section speak to the various and varied aspects of coming to terms with our ever-shifting identities. Whether a name or a pronoun, your gender identity or sexuality – we are perfect just as we are. The trick is to offer ourselves the love and compassion we give to others, and that we deserve.

1D3N+1+Y

Your face and ID does not match.

Title (Ms, Mx, Mr, Br)
Title (Ms, Mx, Mr, Br)
Title (Ms, Mx, Mr, Dr)

Name (as shown on your passport/ID) not match.
Your face and ID does
Please ensure good lighting and a clear background.
Please do not cover any details.
Please do not cover any details.
Name (as shown on your passport/ID)
Please do not cover any details.
Gender (as shown on your passport/ID)

x, Mr, Dr)
x, Mr, Dr)Gender (as shown on your passport/ID)

Please do not cover any details.

Gender (as shown on your passport/ID)

Title (Ms, Mx, Mr, Dr)

Nam
Nam
Nam
Nam
Nam
Nam
Nam
Nam
Nam
Gen
Nam
Nam

Title (Ms, Mx, Mr, Dr) Your face and ID does not match.

Gender (as shown on your passport/ID)

Can you hold your passport/ID to your face?

Please do not cover any details.
Title (Ms, Mx, Mr, Dr)
Title (Ms, Mx, Mr, Dr)
Date of Birth

Please do not cover any details.

Can you hold your passport/ID to your face?
Please ensure good lighting and a clear background.
Please do not cover any details.
Your face and title does not match.
Title (Ms, Mx, Mr, Dr) does not match.
Your face and ID does not match.
Your face and ID does not cover any details.
ur face and ID does not match.
Your face and ID does not match.
Please ensure good lighting and a clear background.
Please ensure good lighting and a clear background.
Gender (as shown on your passport/ID)
r any details.
Please ensure good lighting and a clear background.

Ple
Plea
Y
Ti

Date of Birth

Date of Birth   Title (Ms, Mx, Mr, Dr)

own on your passport/ID)
own on your passport/ID)
own on your passport/ID)
own on your passport/ID)
own on your passport/ID)
own on your passport/ID)
own on your passport/ID)
own on your passport/ID)
own on your passport/ID)
own on your passport/ID)
own on your passport/ID)
nown on your passport/ID)ur passport/ID to your face?
own on your passport/ID)
own on your passport/ID)

Can you hold your passport/ID to your face?

Can you hold your passport/ID to your face?

Can you hold your passport/ID to your face?

lease do not cover any details.
ur face and ID does not match.ld your passport/ID to your face?

t ID does not match.Can you hold your passport/ID to your face?
o not cover any details.
Ms, Mx, Mr, Dr)(as shown on your passport/ID)
and ID does not match.
Mx, Mr, Dr)es not match.
                    Title (Ms, Mx, Mr, Dr)

Winter Chen

Exqueerience

i wish i were a fig wasp,
heavy with purpose and uncomprehending of my place in the chain;
instead i run eggless within fruit,
something on the edge of girlish.
my desires are denied me,
but i cut my hair and feel better,
giddy and euphoric as it falls, auric, to the floor,
and takes my breasts with it.

i do not exist;
mismatched body and soul;
and yet, implausible as opabinia, i must.
i am as much in time as the smilodon,
and see myself in pine shadows and the figure of the lion-man,
undefined and fractal beneath bright light.

when the tides change i am reminded of biology,
the organ-pulse beneath the skin of the earth echoed in my flesh,
pooling crimson tearing tracks down my cheeks.
cringing beneath fluorescence searing skin,
i am sour and sinking,
wolf teeth removed for the bit.

but my heart is away,

beneath starbright and uncaring sky,

where reeds emerge from clear lapping waters to be transmuted to
    goosehomes,

and erica all-powerful runs pink among the sedge.

they say avalon is one big woman;

are people thinking of Her,

as they hike up the folds of Her flesh,

or buy crystals in the warmth of Her womb?

i think people love to align sacred earth with femininity,

to continue abusing its power,

in the name of empowering womanhood.

when you look like a woman, but aren't one,

it loses its appeal;

watching people flock to the fertile, verdant green,

and regard you with the same eye.

Phoebe Trott

You didn't go to prom with me

because I didn't ask. There was something untold
about it, about being country-bound without
knowing it, about eating cheesy rolls on the outskirts
of school bounds. I wonder if me never asking
made you think I wasn't proud to live
under your skin, tucked gently in your breast pocket
like a beakless canary. I understand it better now
but I will never forget the silence that night
where I could hear their music from your room
could see the formless glittering of goodbye girls
escaping from the heat of a school made a kiln.
I slept beside you on your twin-sized mattress
wondering how to tell you, how to ask you, to say:
I would take you to any prom, as long as you'd
dance with me, as long as you'd be fine with it,
as long as everyone forgot we were right there.

Caitlin Tina Jones

Mirror Boy

I am in the theatre dressing room
sixteen years old

black trousers, crisp white shirt
braces firm against my shoulders

bird body preparing to hold its own
launch itself from a nest of props & musky costumes

I run my hands down the seam of my trousers

you can play this part

the mirror boy looks at me
& he is handsome

you are good
at this part

I beam at him like a newborn
he is so lovely
a lovely thing

I reach for my black trilby
& sit it on my head

like a crown

Jaime Lock

On the Run

but don't you see
you cannot outrun this
it is the running that drains you
not the truth

don't you see
there's no finish line
there doesn't need to be

don't you see the community
willing and ready
with open arms and hearts
and labels that fit

slow down,
darling
you already belong
don't you see?

Nicoletta Poungias

Not Your GBF

Will not come the clicks
and whistles you expect.
Will not hold your shopping
when you scramble for
the keys to your apartment door.
You say 'I've always wanted one'
and my mouth pulls open.
For I am no doll to a shelf
no dancing answer
but I am quite simply myself.
I will listen to your chatty
mouth as you empty out
your secrets. I will be open
and honestly speechless
when you tell me
how he mistreated you.
I will be your gay best friend
if perhaps you
learn about me reciprocal
not tokenized but ready for meaning
with you, humanized even.
If we earn it.

Louis Glazzard

Red, Red, Red

When I was a boy,
I wanted to be red,
the brightest colour of a flame.
Drawn in Crayola fire engine red
or the most alluring leaf,
holding on even as October buckles
the dark days of winter coming.

When I was a boy,
I wanted to be Clifford.
I wanted to be Chicago Bulls.
I wanted to be a red convertible,
the one all the other boys wanted.
Oh how, I wanted them to covet me.

I wanted to be rouged cheeks.
I wanted to paint my lips in Revlon.
Just like Mom.

I wanted to be the red of anger.
I wanted to be a lady in red.
I wanted to bleed red:

drip

        drip

                drip.

When I was a boy,
I wanted nothing more
than the most dangerous of colours

to stop

        stop

                stop

the blue inside, but roses are red,
and cherries are red
and quiet boys stay blue.

Left with red lipstick-stained cheeks,
how tired mothers choose to console
telling these boys enough.

It's time to be brave.
It's time to stop crying.
It's time to make some friends.

Remember this isn't dying . . .

it's all about growing up.

So, stop

        stop

                stop.

Or you'll stain your cheeks
But Mom . . .
No, enough, I said.

She left me there to wonder:
Why does pain make us go red
when all boys ever feel is blue?

Andrés N. Ordorica

Playground Games

Muddied park paths in British summer time are
more brown than green and we, blue and pink,
skip through the motions like
we are playing house. Do you remember those
wendy houses? Plastic manic things
too gaudy to love, but that was all I wanted
to be. A façade in the periphery
of some story I would never read.
I would never resort to honesty
and I would never kiss a boy
and I would never not be a boy
and I would never.

Aaron Cawood

Shaping Staff

The first thing I learned at university
was that boiled sausages are almost healthy—
an alternative to their fried selves.
They taste similar, but now their skins slick off:

sad and prophylactic. I would like to see
what forces could do the same weird thing to me,
make me guiltless and lean, and let me shed my skin.

If I picked a shape I think I'd like to be
a snake, a milk snake, or really any form
of lovable snake. I'd leave ghosts of myself
everywhere. I'd leave them like you leave footprints.

Toby Buckley

60% of bisexual people are in psychological distress at any one time

The scalloped edge of the bra means the Roman sun burns my skin into a wave pattern. Once, we were on the beach we had made from the sandbox in your garden. Once, your boobs sat in this bra, not quite filling it, an electric gap between you and the lace. The lawn had been mowed, sweet smell escaping. We tried each other out for size, my pasty flesh spilling out your bikini top as we sat in the mosaic sun of your patio. Your aunt inside the house, hoping its tidy perfection would rub off on her mind. Your father, trampling across the grass cuttings, leaving upon seeing the sight of us, declaring he didn't want a heart attack at forty. Free of those oppressive white walls, we laughed and laughed, our torsos shaped around each other like cuttings bent for a trellis. Now, my burn still aches with the touch of you, my skin less hot from the sun than when your fingers left their mark upon it

Elspeth Wilson

Gender Keeps Me Up at Night

It's not that we're all born
genderless,
though we are.

Rather, once we were all small
women inside our mothers.

Something about science
& sex organs;
hormones & god.

Sasha Torchinsky

Seahorse

Oh how I wish to be a seahorse,
A cute little dragon, only small.
An odd little thing, if you think about it,
Or in hindsight not odd at all.

Here's a fact about seahorses:
The males give birth to their young.
A wonderful thing, if you think about it,
How they carry on with things, and no one's stung.

Charlie Castelletti

Top Surgery

Two lines of light, wounds
open

The past drops out – a cluster
of red stars –

from my chest and onto
the table; metal instruments
latex vinyl wrapped trained hands, mopped brows, pie
slices of artificial brightness above. I look

down at the flat plain, new
man

and ask the air: *is this mine?*
all of it – every inch of scar and –
Yes,
the voice carrying me says. *This is your chest.*

William Keohane

My Gender

A cookbook half-open on the couch
that blows the soft herbs drip in sensual memory
coming hither on the teeth
the way the coconut and its milk
announce themselves exactly as they are
its solids on the fingers.
I would like to substitute myself
thoughtfully, as when forgetting
to pick up cilantro and so basil instead
infusing the meal
at the last minute, when it all seems
like it could be too late,
a little change, a swap, into the same but—
It's silly to make this into an equation,
but here, scribbled on the counter
as I cook dinner for only myself,
no one here to see how I stir,
how I adapt what I've been given,
the recipe as it should be, and fine that way,
and how I've always been taught to eat it,
but then to learn I prefer this other way.

Jason Purcell

A Love Affair with They/Them/Theirs

They mouth poems. They eat raspberries. They dance in the kitchen to a nostalgic video on loop. They watch their favorite anime in their shared two bedroom apartment. They hold cats and asterisks. They kiss them on their lips & they kiss them on their lips back. They blooms & blooms. They write love letters to them & they, occasionally, will too write back. They are unconcerned with distinguishing who's who or definitions. They aren't finite energy: they moves, a fluctuation. Along their back, they curve their fingers, tracing spines and rivers there. Along their fingers, senses pulse, a pattern in their skin cells. They flux through their life for years—through Instagram, through phone calls, texts. Their first date was a Skype call where they watched them play with their cat, and they played with their cat too. The way they each dangled the string was love at first sight for both of them. Both of them are their own truth, their own self, their own beauty. They complement each other beautifully. They compliment their eyes. They compliment their ass. They compliment their smiles. They kiss under the moonlight and the moon lights on their lips.

Brody Parrish Craig

My Gender is not a Controversial Topic

There is no box for me,
No place for me at the table of gender.
It is either this or that,
M or F.

I do not exist, I am a ghost.
A lie that you have repeated,
so many times,
that it sounds like gospel.

My body is a protest,
A place of war and suffering.
The mirror my enemy,
The dark my friend.

You call my name.
It was a name gifted to me,
A gift that weighs on me like a curse.
My name, an echo of a person.

Charlie Brodie

Positive Visibility

There was a spark of hope
that grew brighter inside a dark crowded room.
All of my masked anxiety was starting to clear up,

then the floor beneath my feet crumbled from a roar,

a tasty drum beat that bellowed below a ferocious guitar,
that travelled far, vibrating through every parked car.
There was relief despite my usual idle gloom.
I felt the floodlights rolling in,

it took the form of an aurora

stronger than the evening moon.
The lead singer was decorated in its hues,
rocking out at the centre stage,
strumming their guitar like a powerful mage.
It was refreshing to see a trans person in the spotlight
as the progress flag flowed gracefully behind them.
It was a sight I never thought I would see in the metal scene,
an empowering kind of representation that means so much to me.
I grew up around this hard and heavy kind of music,
so seeing someone like myself was therapeutic.

Aidan Summers

Queer Magic

There are moments when I wish I wasn't transgender
but in those minutes I remind myself
That trans people are magical

That living authentically
in a world that takes every opportunity
to squeeze you uncomfortably into a box
of someone else's design,
That is the most radical act of self love.

Blossoming in an environment
where the odds are stacked so immeasurably against you
is the most beautiful act of defiance.
Wild and vivid like violets
you thrive stubbornly,
bold, between cracked grey pavement.

Because when people live and are celebrated,
Truly embraced and elevated
As themselves
Their *whole* selves
They radiate the purest form of joy I have ever witnessed.
Bright white starlight emanating deep from within
It graces everything it touches,
Warms the skin of those lucky enough to bask in it

And shines a beacon of hope to those yet to flourish.
In those minutes I remind myself
that I am not alone.
I carry with me the dreams of those that came before
in a vessel made of stardust.
One that I can choose to reforge,
in fires of my own making.

I remind myself
That *we* are magical
And we are untouchable
Not unlovable.

We are part of a legacy that will never die
One that will continue long after we are gone.

For We exist
And shall continue
As we have always existed.

Theo Parish

Not Quite Yet

How can I march at Pride
if no one thought to check
if there were stairs? I want
to shout and move amongst
the rainbow flags fluttering
in the wind with my community,
not watch them from above,
there but not there; belonging
but not belonging. How can I
not get overwhelmed without
a space for quiet, to regulate,
to come back to my queer self,
my disabled self, amongst the noise?
How can I be a part of the community
if I'm kept out? Not on purpose –
I'm included, most of the time
on paper, but not fully, not quite
yet. It's Nothing About Us
Without Us, unless we're part
of another group, who sometimes
forget we even exist. I don't, though,
my eyes can't look away from the
beautiful rainbows flying in the wind
while I'm alone, discarded, grounded.

Chloe Smith

How To Be You

From first experiences and experimentation, to the societal pressures put on us, the poems in this section show us the many different ways in which we can exist. Expressing the feelings that bubble to the surface is only half the battle. Being ourselves, as authentically as we possibly can, now that is the real challenge . . .

Self-Portrait with an iPhone

after Will Harris

I pay close attention to
my smile. Many are surprised
to hear of my depression,
there are no selfies of
me crying in bed. Thanks to
Tyra Banks' *America's Next Top Model*,
I have perfected the smize
– smiling with the eyes – it looks
so genuine, I could be
a top model even at rock bottom.

There will be questions:
How are you?
What are you working on?
How are things with Tom?
People only know
what I decide to share
and mostly it's glossy
as a magazine cover.
I have a positive attitude
online and when I go outside.
I prepare myself for
these interactions.

I say *I'm busy*
rather than *I'm overwhelmed.*
I say *I'm excited*
rather than *I'm anxious.*
I say *I'm in love*
rather than *I'm terrified*
of how much I depend on him
for my happiness.

When I open my mouth, I play down
what I'm feeling
behind the smile
perfected for selfies and social situations.
When I look back through all my selfies,
I believe I could be happy.

Dean Atta

The World Well Lost IV

The cheat deceives the cheat, the vain the vain,
the blind the blind, the weak the weak.

Because our world has music, and we dance;
Because our world has colour, and They gaze;
Because our speech is tuned, and schooled our glance,
And we have roseleaf nights and roseleaf days,
And we have leisure, work to do, and rest;
Because They see us laughing when we meet,
And hear our words and voices, see us dressed
With skill, and pass us and our flowers smell sweet:–
They think that we know friendship, passion, love!
Our peacock, Pride! And Art our nightingale!
And Pleasure's hand upon our dogskin glove!
And if they see our faces burn or pale,
    It is the sunlight, think They, or the gas.
    – Our lives are wired like our gardenias.

Marc-André Raffalovich

working out – maybe 2 days a week

I run the length of some never-ending treadmill pay a monthly subscription to exhaust myself while I listen to taylor swift ariana grande dua lipa hilary duff hannah montana and the high school musical soundtrack yes I'm that bitch but this is the noise that gives me motivation to cope the gym-bros stare in confusion the hot girls ignore me I want to be anywhere but here of course but this is what it takes to look a certain way and feel comfortable in my day-to-day existence because that's what society says until I get home and eat 20 chicken nuggets for protein and maybe even a slice of leftover pizza yum

Here I am again running the length of the same never-ending treadmill only this time it's the one adjacent to the window because hench man over there has taken up my usual spot I am still listening to taylor swift ariana grande dua lipa etc but the routine of it all has made me tired I play phantom of the opera instead to perk me up suddenly I am whisked away into a watery lair full of candelabras it feels very chic to be running with these thoughts the timer hits 30 minutes and I rush home to eat a babybel for protein and decide I will never be going back to the gym because I absolutely hate it there

Charlie Castelletti

The Law Concerning Mermaids

There was once a law concerning mermaids. My friend thinks it a wondrous thing – that the British Empire was so thorough it had invented a law for everything. And in this law it was decreed: were any to be found in their usual spots, showing off like dolphins, sunbathing on rocks – they would no longer belong to themselves. And maybe this is the problem with empires: how they have forced us to live in a world lacking in mermaids – mermaids who understood that they simply were, and did not need permission to exist or to be beautiful. The law concerning mermaids only caused mermaids to pass a law concerning man: that they would never again cross our boundaries of sand; never again lift their torsos up from the surf; never again wave at sailors, salt dripping from their curls; would never again enter our dry and stifling world.

Kei Miller

Affirmations for Bisexual Humans

YOU DO NOT OWE ANYONE YOUR 'PERCENTAGES' OR YOUR SEXUAL HISTORY. YOU DO NOT HAVE TO BE IN A SAME-SEX RELATIONSHIP (NOW, OR EVER). YOU DON'T OWE ANYONE AN EXPLANATION ABOUT YOUR SEXUALITY, IT'S YOURS, YOU DECIDE. BISEXUAL DOESN'T MEAN THE EXCLUSION OF TRANS OR NON-BINARY FOLKS. AND, REMEMBER, YOU ARE NOT A SLUT. YOU ARE NOT INDECISIVE. YOU ARE NOT CLOSETED. YOU ARE NOT GREEDY. YOU ARE NOT A PHASE. BISEXUAL IS BEAUTIFUL.

Charlotte Moore

How to Dance with Hoverflies

Hurry to the garden.
Find fennel and creeping thistle.
Follow that rust-warm hum
to a deceit of hoverflies.

Look past first impressions;
pretending to be something else
might mean survival.
You will know this, soon.

Enjoy the summer.
Wear the dress with tassels, spin.
Move how you like.
Move where you feel taken.

Remember this – the joy,
your mother at an open window –
laughter lifting to the wind,
gentle and bright-bodied.

Jack Cooper

Practice

As a teenager, fencing was the closest thing
I knew to desire, all the girls swapping one

> uniform for another before practice, their white
>
> dresses replaced by breeches. I thought we were

princes in a fairy tale with a twist, since
there were no princesses to be taken, wed.

> As knights, we were told to aim for an imaginary
>
> spot just above our opponent's left breast. Often,

I left a bruise: the blade's tip ricocheting off chestguards
on to flesh. Just as often, I would feel yellow

> blooms of ache where the girl I thought was
>
> beautiful
>
> had pierced my heart. Hours later, I would
>
> transform.

I would head back home with a deepening
sense of dread, my bruises fading to quiet.

Mary Jean Chan

once a marine biologist told me octopuses have three hearts

I wonder what I'd do
      with eight arms, two eyes
           & too many ways to give
               myself away

                see, I only have one heart
         & I know loving a woman can make you crawl
    out from under yourself, or forget
the kingdom that is your body

& what would you say, octopus?
      that you live knowing nobody
         can touch you more
            than you do already

              that you can't punch anything underwater
      so you might as well drape yourself
           around it, bring it right up to your mouth
      let each suction cup kiss what it finds

that having this many hands
means to hold everything
at once & nothing
to hold you back

that when you split
you turn your blood
blue & pour
out more ocean

that you know heartbreak so well
you remove all your bones
so nothing can kill you.

Denice Frohman

First Time Sexting

too young or shy for the real thing
I used the internet to find
another boy my age   both of us
old enough to know what we wanted
wasn't 'ordinary'   that no one
taught it us in schools   but our bodies
seemed drawn towards this thing we couldn't
articulate   and so we described
it to each other   nightly   for hours
what we imagined it might be
what we knew our bodies could do alone
whether they could do the same with
someone else   for months we texted that way
in different schools   hiding at the back
of different English lessons   naming
the places we thought we'd like to meet
each other   which   in truth   were places
we were used to being with ourselves
our bedrooms   the shower cubicle
then   one day   in the rush for lunch
I left my phone out on a table
and someone read the contents to the Year
and I stepped back into a room
covered in the ooze of a secret
split open   and their faces were

red with it   I could see the secret dripping
from their lips   and I grabbed my mobile
which you'd think I'd say was heavier
but it felt lighter somehow   and I ran
outside   and cried   and for the first time ever
refused to go to class
and my phone sat vibrating
in my pocket   like a heartbeat
refusing to be silent   maybe
halfwanting to be discovered

Andrew McMillan

They

what do we eat when a name dies?
yesterday your mother stopped by, but she didn't
recognize me as your friend's friend, the previous one.
what is that about, having a dead friend
in the wallet with a picture of a kidnapped kid?
have you seen my son?
he is short and collects photos of swings.

my short hair isn't professional;
your long hair doesn't prepare you.
between the two of us, we figure out how
to fake we are marionettes, not people.
it's difficult to count the days
since the last time we went out.

what is that about, going out
and not having to explain
you aren't that her
or that thing?

in this, our language,[1]
there exists no plural that doesn't deny me.

[1] our language is spanish. ours, but never quite mine.

Raquel Salas Rivera

A Gay Poem

They asked me if I had a gay poem
So I said 'Straight up, no!
My words don't deviate between straight lines
My poems don't mince their words
Or bend
Or make queer little observations'

They asked me if I had a gay poem
So I answered honestly
That, no, I didn't have any gay poetry
And even if, unthinkably, I did
What would it say about me?

I mean, even presenting the question
Puts me in a precarious position
And how would I even begin to broach the subject
With my own creation?

Like . . . 'Excuse me, poem, are you gay?
Have you grown up contrarily to what I wanted you to say?
I most certainly didn't write you that way
Was it something I said, something I did that turned you?
Maybe I should have peppered your verses
With sport, girls and beer

Maybe as your author I deserted you . . .
Or did another writer turn you queer?'

OK, let's say, hypothetically, that this poem is gay
Maybe it's just a confused poem that needs straightening out
Maybe I could insert verses from Leviticus
Speak over it in tongues
Douse it in holy water
Recite it the Qu'ran
Give it a beat, beat, beat
Boom box blasting out in the street
'Batty poem fi dead, batty poem fi dead
Rip up chi chi poem inna shred'

They asked me if I had a gay poem
And I answered 'No'
But the truth is I didn't know
Until one of my very own poems stepped up
And tapped me on the shoulder
It said, 'Look here Dad/Author
I'm now that much bolder
And I'm not confused
And not alternative
And even though the words I choose to marry with
Make me different
It don't make me any less eloquent

'I don't need to be overly elegant
So maybe that's why I stepped under your gaydar
But why are you so afraid to embrace it?
Face it! It's just another part of me
You can't erase it

'The more you try to label me with your twisted synonyms
The more you say you hate the sinner
And despise the sin
The more you try to clip my words
And stifle my expression
The more I know it's you, not me,
Whose morality should be called into question'

They asked me to read out a poem
They said, 'Choose one of your strongest
One of your best
Choose a poem that don't stand for any foolishness'
And they asked me if I had a gay poem . . .
So I said
Yes.

Keith Jarrett

from **A Queerification**

for Creativity and Crisis at the National Mall

queer me

shift me

transgress me

tell my students i'm gay

tell chick fil a i'm queer

tell the new york times i'm straight

tell the mail man i'm a lesbian

tell american airlines

i don't know what my gender is

like me

liking you

like summer blockbuster armrest dates

armrest cinematic love

elbow to forearm in the dark

Regie Cabico

non-binary completionist

Give me the checklist;
the agenda never sent.
To earn my rightful and honest they/them,
tell me which parts I must uproot.
I'll shave my skin and chin and jaw.
I've never had much of an Adam's apple
but maybe I could shave that down too,
and shake myself until the testosterone
comes loose and I can replace it with
softer things. I never wore watches,
only charm bracelets and trinket rings,
but I can switch out the wardrobe
to let my abdomen swim.
I'll dye my hair or
burn it clean, whichever
suits. I'm careful with my cuticles
and my makeup is careful too.
Tell me how I can make myself
into something binary for you.

Aaron Cawood

Criss-Cross

X marks the place
of childhood games.

Eyes digging into
the play of my clothes;
long dress – my mermaid tail,
ruffle, frill – the base of a cake,
velvet, tulle, against my skin.
Home.

There's A-line I will not cross,
But with a pencil write me up. Send tweet.
Heels worn, an absent mother. Raise me through adulthood.

Dig me up,
with your shovel of opinions,
fork that knows all,
Your spade that seeks to define me.

Criss-cross
X marks the
Dresser that I am,
Worth more than buried treasure.
Now swapped for cash and melted down.
I know my worth.

An heirloom of this earth.

You've never struck gold.

Charlie Castelletti

Advice

For those of us in need of some advice, the poems in this section speak to some of the worries we might find ourselves thinking about. They offer hope, wisdom and a little love and guidance as we journey through our days.

Tips to Begin With

1. Spend more time in the worlds in your mind when you don't feel like speaking

2. Hold the parts of yourself that you don't want anyone else to hold

3. Let them cry on your shoulder

4. Let yourself cry on shoulders

5. Allow yourself to see which of your imaginings already exist beyond you

6. Know that it is okay to allow someone else to hold you, and the worlds you hold

David Ly

To the Young Person . . .

wounds need air

to heal, remember

when you're falling

air's

all around you

Peter Scalpello

What I Always Wanted Poetry to Tell Me

Hey, being gay is fine – it is actually quite lovely and warm,
and here is this woman I have fallen for, here are descriptions
of her that will make you cry with relief, see stars of desire.
And oh, god, the human body is wonderful: all hair and sweat,
round like a planet or slack as a river, it is life and history
and poetry and yours will be a miracle to someone, someday,
and it is fine for it to change, fine for your mind to change,
and did I mention it is just gorgeous and brilliant being gay?
It can be soft and careful, or it can be the ocean and fire,
and you are welcome to read my accounts of it with hands
between your thighs – nothing is dirty inside you, I swear,
it is okay to search yourself to find an answer, find many.
This is how I have got here intact, how I fought the pain,
so please – stay. You have something to offer, I guarantee it.

Elizabeth Gibson

To a Son Growing Up

I'll stand aside and bow my head
to let you pass. This is a wild voyage.
My fear might hold you back. Instead
I wish you well, unstrapping my luggage
from your shoulders, becoming my mother
packing sweets for school trips, with *Don't forget
to phone*. Travel light. Slip other
numbers in your pocket beside mine. Get
ready to unfold that map
drawn across your palm, written in your
fingerprints. My wary advice will drop
away like rain when you shake your hair.
You're leaving a bay where it's chill and
early. Your steps are the first on the sand.

Robert Hamberger

dear friend

if you're near,
i'm standing on a winter ledge
bracing winter air.
dear friend,
if you care enough to wake me when you're tired,
if you've seen enough to know enough
to hose down a fire
i am hot on the edge,
and waiting for a reason
to stand up and defeat my demons.
dear friends, dear hands,
stop writing yourself letters.
take a break from your endeavor
to sew yourself together.
you're too busy pressing start
to keep the gameplay in motion.

friend,
if you're lost enough to join me in my zoning,
and you know a thing or two
about sporadic serotonin
come and grab me by the ankles
staple wings to my feet
in my pockets find the keys,
they are jingling eternities.
our hands can forget how to build without each other.
we can make believe we're one step short of lovers.

Ryan Douglass

The Hopes

They extend above the houses
like mechanical giraffes.

Dignified,
they are there for a reason.

Cables hang
from their heads like harnesses.

Behind them, the sky is unusually
blue and clear

for a month so late
in the year. Don't give up.

Colette Bryce

The Unknown

It's scary.
I am however, always scared.
Scared of demons stalking my home
of who is calling my phone
of dying alone.
All of it, so dauntingly unknown.

So I am scared.

Knowing that just out of reach
could well be a sandy beach but,
what if it's not?
What if it's a long fall, the silence that envelops all
at the end?

So I am scared.

I am more scared of the shadows in my head
than any lurking beneath my bed,
because they are the ones with power.
The power to send me
cowering away from anything,
anywhere
everyone.

So, I am scared.

But the truth is, I've already had more time
than my adolescent lies of being fine would have predicted.
And I have to admit,
I've become addicted to being alive.

So, if I could reach back through time and find
that suburban kid,
too scared to live,
too scared of making a mistake
with too many paths to take,
and all of them
uncertain

I'd say to him, I know you're scared,
you are underprepared, but as the unknown becomes known
slowly you'll grow.
And when the foggy future becomes a crystal present,
you'll be glad of the gift.

The gift from our past self,
specially delivered through the war zone of mental health,
the gift of never giving up.

So, yeah, we are scared,

but we have the power to live,
to stare directly into the unknown,
arms wide
head held high
as if it's the adventure of a lifetime.

Because, it is.

And if you survived long enough to become me,
then I owe it to us
to see who this me could be.

Alex Thornber

As Much As You Can

Even if you can't shape your life the way you want,
at least try as much as you can
not to degrade it
by too much contact with the world,
by too much activity and talk.

Try not to degrade it by dragging it along,
taking it around and exposing it so often
to the daily silliness
of social events and parties,
until it comes to seem a boring hanger-on.

C. P. Cavafy,
translated by Edmund Keeley and Philip Sherrard

A Time to Live

Already, fervent life inclines towards evening;
Breathe your youth,
Time is short from the vine to the press,
From the dawn to the passing of day.

Keep open your soul to the perfumes around you,
To the motion of waves.
Love exertion, hope, pride and love itself;
That is the most profound.

How many have gone from all those beating hearts
To their solitude of rest
Without having drunk the honey or breathed the wind
In the mornings of the earth?

How many have gone who, this evening, resemble
The roots of brambles,
And have not tasted a life where the sun
Displays before sinking?

They have not spread wide their excellence or the gold
With which their hands were full
Here they are, now, in this shade where one sleeps
Without dreams and without breath;

But you, steeped in the vastness of desire,
Live the thrills and ecstasy
That lean over the paths where man must serve
As if your soul were a vase.

Within those games of the day, press to your breast
Life both bitter and wild;
May your mouth sing of joy and love
Like the sound of bees

And then, watch with neither regret nor torment
Transient shores flying away
Having given your heart and consent
To eternal night.

Anna de Noailles
translated by David Paley

How to Come Out as Gay

Don't.
Don't come out unless you want to.
Don't come out for anyone else's sake.
Don't come out because you think
society expects you to.
Come out for yourself.
Come out to yourself.
Shout, sing it.
Softly stutter.
Correct those who say they knew
before you did.
That's not how sexuality works,
it's yours to define.
Being effeminate doesn't make you gay.
Being sensitive doesn't make you gay.
Being gay makes you gay.
Be a bit gay, be very gay.
Be the glitter that shows up
in unexpected places.
Be Typing . . . on WhatsApp
but leave them waiting.
Throw a party for yourself
but don't invite anyone else.
Invite everyone to your party
but show up late or not at all.

If you're unhappy in the closet
but afraid of what's outside,
leave the door ajar and call out.
If you're happy in the closet
for the time being,
play dress up until
you find the right outfit.
Don't worry, it's okay
to say you're gay and later exchange it
for something else that suits you,
fits, feels better.
Watch movies that make it seem
a little less scary:
Beautiful Thing, Moonlight.
Be south-east London council estate,
a daytime dance floor,
his head resting on your shoulder.
Be South Beach, Miami,
night of water and fire,
your head resting on his shoulder.
Be the fabric of his shirt
the muscles in his shoulder, your shoulder.
Be the bricks, be the sand.
Be the river, be the ocean.
Remember your life is not a movie.

Accept you
will be coming out for your whole life.
Accept advice
from people and sources you trust.
If your mother warns you about HIV
within minutes of you coming out,
try to understand that she loves you
and is afraid.
If you come out at fifteen,
this is not a badge of honour,
it doesn't matter what age you come out.
Be a beautiful thing.
Be the moonlight, too.
Remember you have the right to be proud.
Remember you have the right to be you.

Dean Atta

I think you can take a break from working on yourself

I'm saying maybe you're no longer a work in progress. You're the finished piece. This. Right Now. I'm saying that you don't need to always be more patient and not every day is the sort of day where you'll make your bed. I'm saying that self-improvement is good, but so is sitting on the sofa and telling yourself you'll do it next week. It's called balance. Maybe you don't need to stress about watching six hours of reality TV because there's nothing better to do. Because sometimes there really is nothing better to do. And even if there is, it's just nice to switch your brain off – it gets busy in there. And honestly I think everyone is tired of adverts telling us to work harder/faster/smarter/be better/be braver when you actually want to be in bed. And we all know self-improvement is good, but you – right now, the you that sulks when things go wrong and will spend a full 24 hours thinking about whether or not that barista in 2017 actually liked them or was just being polite, that you, is a finished piece.

Charlotte Moore

Survival Guide

No matter how old you are,
it helps to be young
when you're coming to life,

to be unfinished, a mysterious statement,
a journey from star to star.
So break out a box of Crayolas

and draw your family
looking uncomfortably away
from the you you've exchanged

for the mannequin
they named. You should
help clean up, but you're so busy being afraid

to love or not
you're missing the fun of clothing yourself
in the embarrassment of life.

Frost your lids with midnight;
lid your heart with frost;
rub them all over, the hormones that regulate

the production of love

from karmic garbage dumps.
Turn yourself into

the real you
you can only discover
by being other.

Voila! You're free.
Learn to love the awkward silence
you are going to be.

Joy Ladin

These Waves of Your Great Heart

You battling with your own heart, speaking the words of peace in
vain,—

The convulsive waves heave and break, do they not?
They go moaning down the dark shore, bitterly, unabating,
Heavily with weary thud falling falling—into the darkness falling.

O heart!
This is the ocean that is broken (on its surface) with measureless
never-ending unrest.
O heart!
This is the wide and immense ocean : over which who shall sail?
O child!
You that shiver there in the night-wind by the dread white-lipped
shore!

Do you guess how wide this Ocean is?
Do you know how it rolls its waters away beyond the farthest
horizon that you have imagined?
Afar, afar—spreading blue beneath the sun by coasts of calm and
tropic beauty, by coasts of tumbling laughing beauty, by bays
and bars and river-narrow straits?—

This ocean of the heart?—

Afar, afar—or bearing on its breast the great white-sailed ships of the earth, or the broad disc of the moon, or the images of men's homes in unimagined lands?

Thought you, frail phantom roaming by the shore,

Gazing wide into the night—a stranger where you had fancied yourself most at home—

Thought you that this great Ocean was to be like an ornamental water in your garden?

Thought you that you knew whence these convulsive waves?—the winds that stirred them, the deeps where they were born?

Think you they weep your sorrows alone, or shake the ground only under your feet?

Not so! not so!

But ever flowing from afar,

From the immeasurable past, from the illimitable shores of human life for ever flowing—on its margin passionately breaking,

With strange uncipherable meanings, whose words are the myriad years,

With speechless terror and amazement to the children beside it,

With amazement of expanded identity, and the inflow of immortal swift-riding purposes, incontrollable, leading straight to death,

In living procession out of the deep—O child! to you they come,
These waves of your great heart, rolling flowing without end :
Through long long ages, under storm and sunshine, by day and
    night, in indomitable splendor rolling,
At your feet now mournfully breaking.

Edward Carpenter

The Journey

One day you finally knew
what you had to do, and began,
though the voices around you
kept shouting
their bad advice –
though the whole house
began to tremble
and you felt the old tug
at your ankles.
"Mend my life!"
each voice cried.
But you didn't stop.
You knew what you had to do,
though the wind pried
with its stiff fingers
at the very foundations,
though their melancholy
was terrible.
It was already late
enough, and a wild night,
and the road full of fallen
branches and stones.

But little by little,
as you left their voices behind,
the stars began to burn
through the sheets of clouds,
and there was a new voice
which you slowly
recognized as your own,
that kept you company
as you strode deeper and deeper
into the world,
determined to do
the only thing you could do –
determined to save
the only life you could save.

Mary Oliver

Those Who Made Us

To those who made us, and who continue to define us, this section focuses on those who came before, who paved the way and allow us to find ourselves in history. From the incomparable Oscar Wilde and Radclyffe Hall to the war poets Wilfred Owen, Siegfried Sassoon and Robert Graves, through to the more modern W. H. Auden, Langston Hughes and Thom Gunn, we have always existed, and here are the voices that show us so. Listen.

How Do I Love Thee?

I cannot woo thee as the lion his mate,
With proud parade and fierce prestige of presence;
Nor thy fleet fancy may I captivate
With pastoral attitudes in flowery pleasance;
Nor will I kneeling court thee with sedate
And comfortable plans of husbandhood;
Nor file before thee as a candidate . . .
I cannot woo thee as a lover would.

To wrest thy hand from rivals, iron-gloved,
Or cheat them by a craft, I am not clever.
But I do love thee even as Shakespeare loved,
Most gently wild, and desperately for ever,
Full-hearted, grave, and manfully in vain,
With thought, high pain, and ever vaster pain.

Wilfred Owen

Shadwell Stair

I am the ghost of Shadwell Stair.
    Along the wharves by the water-house,
    And through the cavernous slaughter-house,
I am the shadow that walks there.

Yet I have flesh both firm and cool,
    And eyes tumultuous as the gems
    Of moons and lamps in the full Thames
When dusk sails wavering down the pool.

Shuddering the purple street-arc burns
    Where I watch always; from the banks
    Dolorously the shipping clanks
And after me a strange tide turns.

I walk till the stars of London wane
    And dawn creeps up the Shadwell Stair.
    But when the crowing syrens blare
I with another ghost am lain.

Wilfred Owen

My Sad Captains

One by one they appear in
the darkness: a few friends, and
a few with historical
names. How late they start to shine!
but before they fade they stand
perfectly embodied, all

the past lapping them like a
cloak of chaos. They were men
who, I thought, lived only to
renew the wasteful force they
spent with each hot convulsion.
They remind me, distant now.

True, they are not at rest yet,
but now they are indeed
apart, winnowed from failures,
they withdraw to an orbit
and turn with disinterested
hard energy, like the stars.

Thom Gunn

Who Ever Loved That Loved Not at First Sight?

From *Hero and Leander*

It lies not in our power to love or hate,
For will in us is overruled by fate.
When two are stripped, long ere the course begin,
We wish that one should love, the other win;

And one especially do we affect
Of two gold ingots, like in each respect.
The reason no man knows; let it suffice,
What we behold is censured by our eyes.
Where both deliberate, the love is slight;
Who ever loved, that loved not at first sight?

Christopher Marlowe

The Foreboding

Looking by chance in at the open window
   I saw my own self seated in his chair
With gaze abstracted, furrowed forehead,
   Unkempt hair.

I thought that I had suddenly come to die,
   That to a cold corpse this was my farewell,
Until the pen moved slowly on the paper
   And tears fell.

He had written a name, yours, in printed letters
   One word on which bemusedly to pore:
No protest, no desire, your naked name,
   Nothing more.

Would it be tomorrow, would it be next year?
   But the vision was not false, this much I knew;
And I turned angrily from the open window
   Aghast at you.

Why never a warning, either by speech or look,
   That the love you cruelly gave me could not last?
Already it was too late: the bait swallowed,
   The hook fast.

Robert Graves

Absence

Sometimes I know the way
  You walk, up over the bay;
It is a wind from that far sea
That blows the fragrance of your hair to me.

Or in this garden when the breeze
  Touches my trees
To stir their dreaming shadows on the grass
  I see you pass.

In sheltered beds, the heart of every rose
  Serenely sleeps to-night. As shut as those
Your guarded heart; as safe as they from the beat, beat
Of hooves that tread dropped roses in the street.

    Turn never again
    On these eyes blind with a wild rain
  Your eyes; they were stars to me.—
    There are things stars may not see.

But call, call, and though Christ stands
  Still with scarred hands
Over my mouth, I must answer. So
I will come—He shall let me go!

Charlotte Mew

Funeral Blues

Stop all the clocks, cut off the telephone,
Prevent the dog from barking with a juicy bone,
Silence the pianos and with muffled drum
Bring out the coffin, let the mourners come.

Let aeroplanes circle moaning overhead
Scribbling on the sky the message 'He is Dead'.
Put crepe bows round the white necks of the public doves,
Let the traffic policemen wear black cotton gloves.

He was my North, my South, my East and West,
My working week and my Sunday rest,
My noon, my midnight, my talk, my song;
I thought that love would last forever: I was wrong.

The stars are not wanted now; put out every one,
Pack up the moon and dismantle the sun,
Pour away the ocean and sweep up the wood;
For nothing now can ever come to any good.

W. H. Auden

One Year After

I

Not once in all our days of poignant love,
Did I a single instant give to thee
My undivided being wholly free.
Not all thy potent passion could remove
The barrier that loomed between to prove
The full supreme surrendering of me.
Oh, I was beaten, helpless utterly
Against the shadow-fact with which I strove.
For when a cruel power forced me to face
The truth which poisoned our illicit wine,
That even I was faithless to my race
Bleeding beneath the iron hand of thine,
Our union seemed a monstrous thing and base!
I was an outcast from thy world and mine.

II

Adventure-seasoned and storm-buffeted,
I shun all signs of anchorage, because
The zest of life exceeds the bound of laws.
New gales of tropic fury round my head
Break lashing me through hours of soulful dread;
But when the terror thins and, spent, withdraws,
Leaving me wondering awhile, I pause–
But soon again the risky ways I tread!
No rigid road for me, no peace, no rest,
While molten elements run through my blood;
And beauty-burning bodies manifest
Their warm, heart-melting motions to be wooed;
And passion boldly rising in my breast,
Like rivers of the Spring, lets loose its flood.

Claude McKay

A Girl

A Girl,
    Her soul a deep-wave pearl
Dim, lucent of all lovely mysteries;
    A face flowered for heart's ease,
    A brow's grace soft as seas
    Seen through faint forest-trees:
    A mouth, the lips apart,
Like aspen-leaflets trembling in the breeze
    From her tempestuous heart.
    Such: and our souls so knit,
    I leave a page half-writ—
       The work begun
Will be to heaven's conception done,
      If she come to it.

Michael Field

Speculation

If at some future day we two should meet,
Stand face to face before the staring crowd,
And pull from Love's dead form the decent shroud
That time has wound about from head to feet—
I scarcely know what words would come to greet
Your presence, if they would be soft or loud,
Would your head be held high or humbly bowed,
And would the moment bitter be or sweet
To me, as you pushed back the long past years,
Would I rejoice, perhaps, at this new pain ?
At least 'twould mean that I could live again,
And had not washed away my soul with tears.
I think there might be much that I could bless
In that deliverance out of nothingness.

Radclyffe Hall

We Two

What have we missed, we two—
You and I—I and you—
Of sorrow, and pain, and tears,
Of doubt, and of passionate fears,
Of madness, and badness, these years!
And what have we missed, we two!

But what have we missed, we two—
You and I—I and you—
Of rapture, and vast delight,
Of loving, and living, of right
To surrender, that love may requite,
How much have we missed, we two!

Radclyffe Hall

Tired

I am so tired of waiting,
Aren't you,
For the world to become good
And beautiful and kind?
Let us take a knife
And cut the world in two-
And see what worms are eating
At the rind.

Langston Hughes

The Way That Lovers Use

The way that lovers use is this;
  They bow, catch hands, with never a word,
And their lips meet, and they do kiss,
  – So I have heard.

They queerly find some healing so,
  And strange attainment in the touch;
There is a secret lovers know,
  – I have read as much.

And theirs no longer joy nor smart,
  Changing or ending, night or day;
But mouth to mouth, and heart on heart,
  – So lovers say.

Rupert Brooke

from The Last Meeting

It was quite still; the columned chestnuts stood
Dark in their noble canopies of leaves.
I thought: 'A little longer I'll delay,
And then he'll be more glad to hear my feet,
And with low laughter ask me why I'm late.
The place will be too dim to show his eyes,
But he will loom above me like a tree,
With lifted arms and body tall and strong.'

There stood the empty house; a ghostly hulk
Becalmed and huge, massed in the mantling dark,
As builders left it when quick-shattering war
Leapt upon France and called her men to fight.
Lightly along the terraces I trod,
Crunching the rubble till I found the door
That gaped in twilight, framing inward gloom.
An owl flew out from under the high eaves
To vanish secretly among the firs,
Where lofty boughs netted the gleam of stars.
I stumbled in; the dusty floors were strewn
With cumbering piles of planks and props and beams;
Tall windows gapped the walls; the place was free
To every searching gust and jousting gale;
But now they slept; I was afraid to speak,
And heavily the shadows crowded in.

I called him, once; then listened: nothing moved:
Only my thumping heart beat out the time.
Whispering his name, I groped from room to room.

Quite empty was that house; it could not hold
His human ghost, remembered in the love
That strove in vain to be companioned still.

Siegfried Sassoon

Two Loves

I dreamed I stood upon a little hill,
And at my feet there lay a ground, that seemed
Like a waste garden, flowering at its will
With buds and blossoms. There were pools that dreamed
Black and unruffled; there were white lilies
A few, and crocuses, and violets
Purple or pale, snake-like fritillaries
Scarce seen for the rank grass, and through green nets
Blue eyes of shy pervenche winked in the sun.
And there were curious flowers, before unknown,
Flowers that were stained with moonlight, or with shades
Of Nature's wilful moods; and here a one
That had drunk in the transitory tone
Of one brief moment in a sunset; blades
Of grass that in an hundred springs had been
Slowly but exquisitely nurtured by the stars,
And watered with the scented dew long cupped
In lilies, that for rays of sun had seen
Only God's glory, for never a sunrise mars
The luminous air of Heaven. Beyond, abrupt,
A grey stone wall, o'ergrown with velvet moss,
Uprose; and gazing I stood long, all mazed
To see a place so strange, so sweet, so fair.
And as I stood and marvelled, lo! across
The garden came a youth; one hand he raised

To shield him from the sun, his wind-tossed hair
        Was twined with flowers, and in his hand he bore
   A purple bunch of bursting grapes, his eyes
Were clear as crystal, naked all was he,
        White as the snow on pathless mountains frore,
  Red were his lips as red wine-spilth that dyes
A marble floor, his brow chalcedony.
        And he came near me, with his lips uncurled
   And kind, and caught my hand and kissed my mouth,
And gave me grapes to eat, and said, 'Sweet friend,
        Come, I will show thee shadows of the world
   And images of life. See from the South
Comes the pale pageant that hath never an end.'
        And lo! within the garden of my dream
   I saw two walking on a shining plain
        Of golden light. The one did joyous seem
   And fair and blooming, and a sweet refrain
        Came from his lips; he sang of pretty maids
   And joyous love of comely girl and boy;
        His eyes were bright, and 'mid the dancing blades
   Of golden grass his feet did trip for joy;
        And in his hand he held an ivory lute
   With strings of gold that were as maidens' hair,
        And sang with voice as tuneful as a flute,
   And round his neck three chains of roses were.
        But he that was his comrade walked aside;

He was full sad and sweet, and his large eyes
    Were strange with wondrous brightness, staring wide
With gazing; and he sighed with many sighs
    That moved me, and his cheeks were wan and white
Like pallid lilies, and his lips were red
    Like poppies, and his hands he clenchèd tight,
And yet again unclenchèd, and his head
    Was wreathed with moon-flowers pale as lips of death.
A purple robe he wore, o'erwrought in gold
    With the device of a great snake, whose breath
Was like curved flame: which when I did behold
    I fell a-weeping, and I cried, 'Sweet youth,
Tell me why, sad and sighing, thou dost rove
    These pleasent realms? I pray thee, speak me sooth,
What is thy name?' He said, 'My name is Love.'
    Then straight the first did turn himself to me
And cried: 'He lieth, for his name is Shame,
    But I am Love, and I was wont to be
Alone in this fair garden, till he came
    Unasked by night; I am true Love, I fill
The hearts of boy and girl with mutual flame.'
    Then sighing, said the other: 'Have thy will,
I am the love that dare not speak its name.'

Lord Alfred Douglas

Apologia

Is it thy will that I should wax and wane,
  Barter my cloth of gold for hodden grey,
And at thy pleasure weave that web of pain
  Whose brightest threads are each a wasted day?

Is it thy will—Love that I love so well—
  That my Soul's House should be a tortured spot
Wherein, like evil paramours, must dwell
  The quenchless flame, the worm that dieth not?

Nay, if it be thy will I shall endure,
  And sell ambition at the common mart,
And let dull failure be my vestiture,
  And sorrow dig its grave within my heart.

Perchance it may be better so—at least
  I have not made my heart a heart of stone,
Nor starved my boyhood of its goodly feast,
  Nor walked where Beauty is a thing unknown.

Many a man hath done so; sought to fence
  In straitened bonds the soul that should be free,
Trodden the dusty road of common sense,
  While all the forest sang of liberty,

Not marking how the spotted hawk in flight
   Passed on wide pinion through the lofty air,
To where the steep untrodden mountain height
   Caught the last tresses of the Sun God's hair.

Or how the little flower he trod upon,
   The daisy, that white-feathered shield of gold,
Followed with wistful eyes the wandering sun
   Content if once its leaves were aureoled.

But surely it is something to have been
   The best belovèd for a little while,
To have walked hand in hand with Love, and seen
   His purple wings flit once across thy smile.

Ay! though the gorgèd asp of passion feed
   On my boy's heart, yet have I burst the bars,
Stood face to face with Beauty, known indeed
   The Love which moves the Sun and all the stars!

Oscar Wilde

We Are Librarian

We.

We are.

We are librarian.

We are librarian sent from the stars.

We are librarian sent from the stars to take care of you.

We are librarian sent from the stars to take care of you to live in this world.

We are librarian sent from the stars to take care of you to live in this world which is one of so many.

We are librarian sent from the stars to take care of you to live in this world which is one of so many that you can travel to.

We are librarian sent from the stars to take care of you to live in this world which is one of so many that you can travel to only if you stay alive.

Stay alive.

*

Write is the left hand of darkness, and I was reading like it was fire. The sole source of illumination in a childhood of silences, denials, and violence. I had learned to read the signs, to judge a book under the covers, to listen for hints and take them, let them take me; preferably as far away as possible.

Whispers in the bookstacks
Remind me, baby, of you.

This is what I remember finding. What I remember finding me.

The Sandman
The Man who Fell in Love With the Moon
Giovanni's Room
Goodbye to Berlin
Interview with a Vampire
Desert of the Heart

Faced out without comment, on the dinted, chipped cream metal shelves of Edgware Library by who. No librarian could put their name to it, not under Section 28 of the Local Government Act (1988).

A trail of bread crumbs to the House of Gingerbread.

What if I want to stay (with) the witch?

So Mayer

The Road from Hebden Bridge

I now have a mug with a quote from Anne Lister,
about loving women, and women loving her back,
and I can pour myself hot chocolate in my little flat,
and let her words, and your words, warm in my fist.
You were right, about this.

You are like me, you said as you drove, *it is okay*.
You told me your story, gave me laughter and grit;
when I dug into doubt, you led me out from my pit,
to green hills and blue sky and lanes full of rosebay.
Trust me, kid. You are gay.

I smiled and smiled, wouldn't let myself hide it.
And as we wandered Shibden, her house, her stables,
your sheet of hair and the hoodie round your waist
were always up ahead, for me to follow and find.
We drove back full and quiet.

You told me again, back at the house by the river,
*you can make a fool of yourself; you will, probably,
but you will find her in the end, and you will be happy*.
We shared some crisps: sea salt and wine vinegar,
your favourite – I still remember.

Elizabeth Gibson

Who Are We Now and Where Will We Be?

How did we get here? How much further do we have to go? Being queer is a constant battle, but with our struggle comes immeasurable love and joy and, ultimately, freedom. This section looks at our past, present and future selves – the ups, the downs, the in-between. Who are we now, and where will we be in years to come? That's up to us.

Briefly, there were books

Briefly, there were books.
Tales of her and her,
him and him,
them.
Us.

Covers in the colors of the rainbow,
reaching from the shelves like flags,
staking their claim,
their right to exist,
calling out to us
and our right to exist.

Dog ears,
broken spines,
food spatters,
loose bindings.

Broken and
beautiful and
beloved.

Books that belonged to us,
while we simply
belonged.

Briefly.

Then
came
the
protests,
laws,
courts,
lies.

Don't say gay.
Don't say they.

The colors dimmed,
the flags uprooted,
the shelves emptied.

They say
the books don't belong to us.
They mean

we
don't
belong.

Boycotted,
Banned,
Burned.

Bereft.
Briefly, there were books.

Jessica Verdi

Not Even

Hey.

I used to be a fag now I'm a checkbox.

The pen tip jabbed in my back, I feel the mark of progress.

I will not dance alone in the municipal graveyard at midnight, blasting sad songs on my phone, for nothing.

I promise you, I was here. I felt things that made death so large it was indistinguishable from air – and I went on destroying inside it like wind in a storm.

The way Lil Peep says *I'll be back in the mornin'* when you know how it ends.

The way I kept dancing when the song was over, because it freed me.

The way the streetlight blinks twice, before waking up for its night shift, like we do.

The way we look up and whisper *Sorry* to each other, the boy and I, when there's teeth.

When there's always teeth, on purpose.

When I threw myself into gravity and made it work. Ha.

I made it out by the skin of my griefs.

I used to be a fag now I'm lit. Ha.

Once, at a party set on a rooftop in Brooklyn for an 'artsy vibe', a young woman said, sipping her drink, *You're so lucky. You're gay plus you get to write about war and stuff. I'm just white.* [Pause] *I got nothing.* [Laughter, glasses clinking]

Because everyone knows yellow pain, pressed into American letters, turns to gold.

Our sorrow Midas touched. Napalm with a rainbow afterglow.

Unlike feelings, blood gets realer when you feel it.

I'm trying to be real but it costs too much.

They say the earth spins and that's why we fall but everyone knows it's the music.

It's been proven difficult to dance to machine-gun fire.

Still, my people made a rhythm this way. A way.

My people, so still, in the photographs, as corpses.

My failure was that I got used to it. I looked at us, mangled under the *Time* photographer's shadow, and stopped thinking, *get up, get up*.

I saw the graveyard steam in the pinkish dawn and knew the dead were still breathing. Ha.

If they come for me, take me out.

What if it wasn't the crash that made us, but the debris?

What if it was meant this way: the mother, the lexicon, the line of cocaine on the mohawked boy's collarbone in an East Village sublet in 2007?

What's wrong with me, Doc? There must be a pill for this.

Because the fairy tales were right. You'll need magic to make it out of here.

Long ago, in another life, on an Amtrak through Iowa, I saw, for a few blurred seconds, a man standing in the middle of a field of winter grass, hands at his sides, back to me, all of him stopped there save for his hair scraped by low wind.

When the countryside resumed its wash of gray wheat, tractors, gutted barns, black sycamores in herdless pastures, I started to cry. I put my copy of Didion's *The White Album* down and folded a new dark around my head.

The woman beside me stroked my back, saying, in a midwestern accent that wobbled with tenderness, *Go on son. You get that out now. No shame in breakin' open. You get that out and I'll fetch us some tea.* Which made me lose it even more.

She came back with Lipton in paper cups, her eyes nowhere blue and there. She was silent all the way to Missoula, where she got off and said, patting my knee, *God is good. God is good.*

I can say it was gorgeous now, my harm, because it belonged to no one else.

To be a dam for damage. My shittyness will not enter the world, I thought, and quickly became my own hero.

Do you know how many hours I've wasted watching straight boys play video games?

Enough.

Time is a mother.

Lest we forget, a morgue is also a community center.

In my language, the one I recall now only by closing my eyes, the word for *love* is *Yêu.*

And the word for *weakness* is *Yê´u.*

How you say what you mean changes what you say.

Some call this prayer, I call it watch your mouth.

Rose, I whispered as they zipped my mother in her body bag, *get out of there.*

Your plants are dying.

Enough is enough.

Time is a motherfucker, I said to the gravestones, alive, absurd.

Body, doorway that you are, be more than what I'll pass through.

Stillness. That's what it was.

The man in the field in the red sweater, he was so still he became, somehow, more true, like a knife wound in a landscape painting.

Like him, I caved.

I caved and decided it will be joy from now on. Then everything
opened. The lights blazed around me into a white weather

and I was lifted, wet and bloody, out of my mother, into the world,
screaming

and enough.

Ocean Vuong

Over the Great City

Over the great city,
Where the wind rustles through the parks and gardens,
In the air, the high clouds brooding,
In the lines of street perspective, the lamps, the traffic,
The pavements and the innumerable feet upon them,
I Am: make no mistake – do not be deluded.

Think not because I do not appear at the first glance – because the
     centuries have gone by and there is no assured tidings of me –
     that therefore I am not there.
Think not because all goes its own way that therefore I do not go
     my own way through all.
The fixed bent of hurrying faces in the street – each turned
     towards its own light, seeing no other – yet I am the Light
     towards which they all look.
The toil of so many hands to such multifarious ends, yet my hand
     knows the touch and twining of them all.

All come to me at last.
There is no love like mine;
For all other love takes one and not another;
And other love is pain, but this is joy eternal.

Edward Carpenter

Erased

the importance of being
witnessed
consumes centuries
when the witness is lost

Sasha Torchinsky

Open

it happens each time   the coming out to a classroom
tepid expressions and frozen eyes
a stagnant silence that rushes towards the door
I pull up the blinds   let them see the undiluted world outside
say see nothing has changed   they blink widely
like they haven't seen it quite like this
before   rose-tint fading to heavy red blotches
throats as caged birds   I unlatch the bars   invite them out
they sing *so when did ya know   how did ya know like*
was it when ya were little   or did ya just turn
one day   I don't think I had a gay teacher at school
at least not that I knew   the veil
never lifted from the lives of those who patrolled corridors
like vultures   they can nose in anytime my door is always open

Dale Booton

I Am the Mob

Lately, even my clavicles
have separate identities and private
YouTube channels. My teeth
keep making death threats
and God knows why my feet
are pretending to be glaciers.
My nipples have fallen out
with each other. My hairs point
accusingly at everything.
Haven't had an email
from my pancreas in forever
and my liver is trapped
in the sixteenth century, enraged
by its imbalance of humours.

Worst of all, I don't own my face.
It floats unannounced into mirrors,
firing lasers like a bitchy spaceship.
How the lot of us get anything done
I have no idea. If it wasn't
for our collective suspicion
about the world outside this body,
frankly we'd be nowhere.

John McCullough

Here Be

In ten years' time you will adopt a dragon. Maybe
from a shelter for unwanted cryptids, or just because
she landed in your back garden looking gorgeous but
a little sad about the nostrils. Either way,

you'll place a dish of charcoal on the kitchen floor
and immediately fall in love with her ankle-spurs,
her eyelashes (softer than the undragoned imagine),
the way she could roast you if she wanted, and might.

You will quickly get used to the smell of singed curtains.
You will move to a top-floor flat so she can practise
dead-drops down the stairwell. You will sing with her,
a tuneless, raucous clatter of song that would send sleepless

neighbours into fury if it weren't so holy.
You will be astonished at the speed your life changes,
at how much time she has eaten, clockwork and all.
It's more than can be explained by her hot

scales through your jodhpurs. Her wings are impossible,
the aerial views in her gift are impossible. She is
impossible. In eleven years' time, you will finger the scar
on your cheek and hope that when she left you –

in flight or through a slit in air's fabric –
she meant to leave you with such a hoard of gold.

Harry Josephine Giles

Pride

There is pride in my bite.
Lipstick smudge on neck,
vampire teeth in,
are you afraid you will turn into me?

There is pride in the bashing,
bashing of my back.
Bash back, to face.
imagine fist into your jeer.

There is pride in the way I yell.
'Who you calling faggot?'
'What the fuck are you looking at?'
'Did you not know that us freaks have mouths?'

There is pride in my heels wandering.
Forceful, stomps on grounds
Pushes into knees that stop
Who knew fear could look this fierce?

There is pride in my flexibility.
To go from death drop
To dancing with death
It is your loss that you only hear my fingers click.

You tell me of pride in rainbows,

In flags and flat stomachs, muscles and chests,

Pride in our celebration,

In unity and glee,

And I spit out my pride in rebellion.

The pride in saying:

I am a freak, and you cannot fuck with me.

Travis Alabanza

Thoughts on Romance as the Heat Index Rises

I open my mouth and, despite the world,
use it almost daily to fall in love.

This is so direly human of me—
so egregiously alive. I feel

lucky to hold my partner's skin
and their hunger on my tongue

always. I am thankful that, most
mornings, the day still opens

its mouth
for both of us.

Kayleb Rae Candrilli

i love you to the moon &

not back, let's not come back, let's go by the speed of
queer zest & stay up
there & get ourselves a little
moon cottage (so pretty), then start a moon garden

with lots of moon veggies (so healthy), i mean
i was already moonlighting
as an online moonologist
most weekends, so this is the immensely

logical next step, are you
packing your bags yet, don't forget your
sailor moon jean jacket, let's wear
our sailor moon jean jackets while twirling in that lighter,

queerer moon gravity, let's love each other
(so good) on the moon, let's love
the moon
on the moon

Chen Chen

Us

It's not a feeling,
It's just knowing
That no matter what we do
There will be us.
The queens of spring,
Fixing each other's crowns,
Protecting each other
From anyone who brings us down.
We are here to cheer each other on
And there is no purer love than this,
The love of sisters who found each other,
Rejoicing in what belongs to us,
Life, a brand new adventure,
Friendship a cathedral we built together
Where our love becomes prayer
Where every laugh is an amen.

Nikita Gill

What Kind of Times Are These

There's a place between two stands of trees where the grass grows
　　uphill
and the old revolutionary road breaks off into shadows
near a meeting-house abandoned by the persecuted
who disappeared into those shadows.

I've walked there picking mushrooms at the edge of dread, but
　　don't be fooled
this isn't a Russian poem, this is not somewhere else but here,
our country moving closer to its own truth and dread,
its own ways of making people disappear.

I won't tell you where the place is, the dark mesh of the woods
meeting the unmarked strip of light—
ghost-ridden crossroads, leafmold paradise:
I know already who wants to buy it, sell it, make it disappear.

And I won't tell you where it is, so why do I tell you
anything? Because you still listen, because in times like these
to have you listen at all, it's necessary
to talk about trees.

Adrienne Rich

By Heart

I made myself imagine that I didn't love you,
that your face was ordinary to me. This was in our house
when you were out, secret, guessing what such difference

would be like, never to have known your touch,
your taste. Then I went out and passed the places
where we'd go, without you there, pretending that I could.

Making believe I could, I tried to blot out longing,
or regret, when someone looked like you, head down,
laughing, running away from me behind a veil of rain.

So it was strange to see you, just ahead of me,
as I trailed up the hill, thinking how I can't unlearn
the words I've got by heart, or dream your name away,

and shouting it, involuntarily, three times, until
you turned and smiled. Love makes buildings home
and out of dreary weather, sometimes, rainbows come.

Carol Ann Duffy

Future

you claim the words
they make sound like a slur
you've come too far
to give up now
your feet already sense
the victory dance ahead
your mind
already caught a glimpse
of the future
its beauty and possibility

you lay down
atop the tumultuous world
listen to its rivers
flowing through your veins
perfectly synchronized
your chest rises
filling your lungs
with life
I know you can make it
I have seen the universe
in your eyes

Nicoletta Poungias

O Me! O Life!

Oh me! Oh life! of the questions of these recurring,
Of the endless trains of the faithless, of cities fill'd with the foolish,
Of myself forever reproaching myself, (for who more foolish than I,
    and who more faithless?)
Of eyes that vainly crave the light, of the objects mean, of the
    struggle ever renew'd,
Of the poor results of all, of the plodding and sordid crowds I see
    around me,
Of the empty and useless years of the rest, with the rest me
    intertwined,
The question, O me! so sad, recurring—What good amid these,
    O me, O life?

Answer.

That you are here—that life exists and identity,
That the powerful play goes on, and you may contribute a verse.

Walt Whitman

239

Steps

What if
I told you
that in some
far away place
not too far
away
there was a
lonely
little person
waiting
just waiting
for someone
exactly like
you
to come into their lives
and show
them

all the ways
all the
many
different ways
all
the
possibilities
and
directions
they have
to decide
which
path
their life
should
take

And
        there
                are
                        so
                                many
                                        places
                                                I
                                        want
                                                to
                                                        see
                                                                us
                                                                        go
                                                                    So many places.

                        And
                                maybe
                                        just maybe
                                                we will reach these places

In our own way. I believe it. We have to believe it. For what other hope do we have

. . . unless we show them . . .

of telling the world who we are? How we live? And all the places we could go . . .

Charlie Castelletti

Now, always, more

and what if we were more of us, more than these
bodies that hold us? what if we were forever in the
bodies we hold the way we hold bodies, our own,
each other's. we could run like machines, never
stopping, like the codes that hold the leaves that
keep them green for us to see and breathe. if i were
you and you were me and we were both each other
we could run together then. forever, and more. we
might know how it feels when bodies become
timeless in their togetherness, nowness, alwaysness
and neverness, without difference - the way you think
of love if love were a machine, running by itself without
anything or anyone to halt its course, if there were all
there could be and we ran with it then life would go
on forever, and we could be now, always, more.

and what if we were less than this, less than whole,
less than full? then we might have more space to
share, more space to fill, more space to become.
wholeness is not allness, and a little less might bring
us allness in the space we do not yet fill, cannot fill
alone. so much space to use by becoming, where
otherwise we may have felt no more could fit or there
was no space to lose beyond what we now hold. spilling
over the brim, outside of time or on its good side. if there

was one. a little bit of less may bring a great deal of more, softness foregone by bodies so eager to fill up every gap, to find the right side of time and stick to it for fear of losing something unsayable or unsaid, a compromise of softness. perhaps in less we may find now, always, more.

and what if none of this mattered, these questions that gnawed away at your brain that you wanted to be free from? what if you already were? what if we were part of this constant movement, ever changing and evolving, like the earth that spins around the sun or the moon that spins around the earth that we never feel? we assume that a change will be overwhelming, all-consuming, destructive, but it can be so subtle, so gentle, as simple and as calm as the end of the world, or a hand holding your own for the first time. peace at last, and nothing more. the little world whose history spans millennia within which you float for a short while, and whose meaning no one can explain with certainty. but once the hand takes yours with such tenderness that you do not even register, you are forever changed, other, both or neither. now, always, more. somehow.

Grace Copeland-Tucker

Fragment 60

And I say to you someone will remember us
In time to come . . .

Sappho,
translated by A. S. Kline

Index of First Lines

A cookbook half-open on the couch 126

A Girl 198

A jug of milk in the fridge 99

A raspberry one with moist frosting, or 89

After Sunday lunch 39

Already, fervent life inclines towards evening 172

And I say to you someone will remember us 246

and if 100

and what if we were more of us, more than these 244

As a teenager, fencing was the closest thing 145

As I lie on my back in the dry grass 96

As I was going down those ill-famed stairs 18

Because our world has music, and we dance 139

Because when they told us 103

Boys in moonlight shine 38

Briefly, there were books 217

but don't you see 115

Can a thunderstorm happen in mid-winter 41

Don't 174

Even if you can't shape your life the way you want 171

For those of us who live at the shoreline 74

Give me the checklist 155

Having a Coke with you 87

Having used every subterfuge 16

He's here in the midst of it 40

Hey 220

Hey, being gay is fine – it is actually quite lovely and warm 163

His face licked by the pink of neon lights 90

"Hope" is the thing with feathers 73

How can I march at Pride 132

How old was I? 48

Hurry to the garden 144

I am in the theatre dressing room 113

I am so tired of waiting 201

I am the ghost of Shadwell Stair 190

I cannot woo thee as the lion his mate 189

I dreamed I stood upon a little hill 205

I lounge in the doorway and languish in vain 35

i love you to the moon & 234

I made myself imagine that I didn't love you 237

I miss the touch of lip to lip 13

I now have a mug with a quote from Anne Lister 212

I open my mouth and, despite the world 233

I pay close attention to 137

I run the length of some 140

I say it so often it's embedded in my skin 70

I tell my hands to loosen 36

I wake up and eat a banana 66

I wasn't born in a girl's body 54

i wish i were a fig wasp 110

I wonder what I'd do 146

If at some future day we two should meet 199

If I could paint you, friend, as you stand there 6

If I could pray the gay away 72

If I could smile 79

if you're near 165

I'll stand aside and bow my head 164

I'm saying maybe you're no longer a work in progress 177

In ten years' time you will adopt a dragon 230

Is it thy will that I should wax and wane 208

It arrives in the kitchen 25

it happens each time the coming out to a classroom 228

It is so easy to imagine your absence 37

It lies not in our power to love or hate 192

It was quite still; the columned chestnuts stood 203

It's not a feeling 235

It's not that we're all born 123

It's scary 168

It's true that I'm im- 53

Just once we met 11

Last time I saw myself die is when police killed Jessie Hernandez 60

Lately, even my clavicles 229

Looking by chance in at the open window 193

Muddied park paths in British summer time are 120

My _____ corseted in whirlpool & whalebone 56

No bus comes this way 7

No matter how old you are 178

Not once in all our days of poignant love 196

Oh how I wish to be a seahorse 124

Oh me! Oh life! of the question of these recurring 239

On days when we'd go to the galleries 31

on the pitch by my house 19

Once, sparks really did ignite from my lips after i kissed him 24

Once when I wasn't, I rang in sick for the evening shift 85

One by one they appear in 191

One day you finally knew 183

Our 17

Over the great city 226

queer me 154

She moves about in the tiny flat 47

Sister, you are smiling when I meet you 67

Slowing down your body enough to feel 65

Some early November mornings ago on Tinder 9

Some months all my thoughts are one colour 95

Sometimes I know the way 194

song of daybreak on the playground 82

Spend more time in the worlds in your mind when you 161

Stop all the clocks, cut off the telephone 195

The first thing I learned at university 121

The green diamond floats above 80

the importance of being 227

The moon is trans 58

The scalloped edge of the bra means the Roman sun burns my 122

The street sounds to the soldiers' tread 63

The unexpected interest made him flush 3

The way that lovers use is this 202

There are moments when I wish I wasn't transgender 130

There is no box for me 128

There is pride in my bite 231

There was a spark of hope 129

There was once a law concerning mermaids 142

there were good days / during the holidays / when your 81

there were street lights 97

There's a place between two stands of trees where the grass grows
uphill 236

There's an iridescent rainbow scatter 93

These I have loved 91

They asked me if I had a gay poem 151

They extend above the houses 167

They mouth poems 127

They say I'm not supposed to love you 46

Title (Ms, Mx, Mr, Dr) 108

To clasp you now and feel your head close-pressed 10

too young or shy for the real thing 148

TURNING TO A FRIEND AND AGREEING 84

Two lines of light, wounds open 125

Up those Museum steps you came 32

Waiting by his side 57

We 210

we met on a Girl Guides trip (she texted first) 45

We passed each other, turned and stopped for half an hour 42

We practise anatomy 12

We two boys together clinging 5

what do we eat when a name dies? 150

What have we missed, we two 200

What if 240

When I was a boy 117

When Sheila flicked up the hood of her cloak 21

Will not come the clicks 116

wounds need air 162

X marks the place 156

You battling with your own heart, speaking the words of peace in
    vain 180

you claim the words 238

You didn't go to prom with me 112

YOU DO NOT OWE ANYONE YOUR 143

You're a gem, you're a holy cairn 101

Your laugh eats up the slurs your dad scattered on your floor 64

Index of Poets and Translators

Alabanza, Travis 231

Atta, Dean 137, 174

Auden, W. H. 195

Bendorf, Oliver Baez 53

Booton, Dale 228

Brantley, Cal 103

Brodie, Charlie 128

Brooke, Rupert 91, 202

Bryce, Colette 47, 167

Buckley, Toby 121

Cabico, Regie 154

Candrilli, Kayleb Rae 233

Carpenter, Edward 180, 226

Castelletti, Charlie 124, 140, 156, 240

Cavafy, C. P. 18, 171

Cawood, Aaron 120, 155

Chan, Mary Jean 145

Chen, Chen 234

Chen, Winter 56, 108

Clancy, Sarah 85

Cooper, Jack 12, 144

Copeland-Tucker, Grace 244

Costa, Luís 57, 90

Craig, Brody Parrish 127

Crane, Hart 3

Custance, Olive 11

Dapanas, Alton Melvar M 9

Day, Kelsey, 25

Dickinson, Emily 73

Dimitrov, Alex 66

Douglas, Alfred, Lord 205

Douglass, Ryan 165

Duffy, Carol Ann 237

Espinoza, Joshua Jennifer 58

Field, Michael 198

Frohman, Denice 146

Gibson, Elizabeth 163, 212

Giles, Harry Josephine 67, 230

Gill, Nikita 46, 235

Gillingham, Erica 31, 97

Glazzard, Louis 116

Graves, Robert 193

Griffin, Eva 99

Gunn, Thom 191

Haigh, Matthew 21

Hall, Radclyffe 199, 200

Hamberger, Robert 48, 164

Hofmann, Richie 37

Housman, A. E. 63

Hughes, Langston 201

Hulme, Jay 40, 70

Jarrett, Keith 151

Jones, Caitlin Tina 112

Kay, Jackie 101

Keeley, Edmund 18, 171

Keohane, William 125

Kline, A. S. 246

Knights, Karl 7, 36

Ladin, Joy 178

Lefroy, Edward Cracroft 6

Levy, Amy 32, 35

Liu, Timothy 65

Lock, Jaime 113

Lorde, Audre 74

Ly, David 24, 161

Marlowe, Christopher 192

Mayer, So 210

McCann, Micheál 89

McCullough, John 95, 229

McKay, Claude 10, 196

McLane, Maureen N. 100

McMillan, Andrew 19, 148

Merrill, James 16

Mew, Charlotte 42, 194

Miller, Kei 142

Moore, Charlotte 84, 143, 177

Morris, Charlie 93

Morris Dixon, Jo 45, 81

Ndaba, Hope 82

Noailles, Anna de 172

Oet, Rainie 41, 54, 79

O'Hara, Frank 87

Oliver, Mary 183

Ordorica, Andrés N. 72, 117

Owen, Wilfred 189, 190

Paley, David 172

Parish, Theo 130

Parnok, Sophia 41

Poungias, Nicoletta 115, 238

Purcell, Jason 126

Raffalovich, Marc-André 139

Rich, Adrienne 236

Salas Rivera, Raquel 150

Sappho 246

Sassoon, Siegfried 203

Scalpello, Peter 162

Sherrard, Philip 18, 171

Smith, Chloe 132

Soto, Christopher 60

Summers, Aidan 129

Taylor, Rosamund 96

Tempest, Kae 17

Thornber, Alex 168

Torchinsky, Sasha 123, 227

Trott, Phoebe 110

Verdi, Jessica 217
Vuong, Ocean 220
Whitman, Walt 5, 239
Wilde, Oscar 208
Wilson, Elspeth 64, 80, 122
Woods, Gregory 38, 39
Woolf, Freja Nicole 13

Copyright Acknowledgements

Sappho: from *Selected Poems and Fragments* by Sappho (Author), A. S. Kline (Translator), Copyright © 2005; **Alabanza, Travis:** 'Pride' © Travis Alabanza. First published in the *Gay Times* and reproduced with permission of David Godwin Associates; **Atta, Dean:** 'Self Portrait with an iPhone' and 'How to Come Out as Gay' reproduced by kind permission of Lewisohn Literary Limited; **Auden, W.H:** 'Funeral Blues' Copyright © 1940 by W. H. Auden, renewed. Reprinted by permission of Curtis Brown, Ltd. All rights reserved; **Baez Bendof, Oliver:** 'Dysphoria' First published in Academy of American Poets' Poem-a-Day. Reproduced by permission of the author; **Booton, Dale:** 'Open' Reprinted by permission of the author; **Brantley, Cal:** 'An Ode to Trans Bodies' Reprinted by permission of the author; **Brodie, Charlie:** 'My Gender is Not a Controversial Topic' Reprinted by permission of the author; **Bryce, Colette:** 'The Hopes' from Self Portrait in the Dark (Picador, 2008) and 'Words and Music' from The Full Indian Rope Trick (Picador, 2004) Reproduced by permission of the publisher; **Buckley, Toby:** 'Shaping Staff' Reproduced by permission of the author; **Cabico, Regie:** from 'A Queerification', Reproduced by permission of the author; **Candrilli, Kayleb Rae:** 'Thoughts on Romance as the Heat Index Rises' *All the Gay Saints*, Saturnalia Books, May 5th, 2020. Reprinted by permission of the author; **Castelletti, Charlie:** 'Seahorse', 'Steps', 'going to the gym – maybe 2 days a week' and 'Criss-Cross' Reproduced by permission of the author; **Cavafy, Constantine:** 'As Much as You Can' and 'On the Stairs' from *C. P. CAVAFY: Collected Poems Revised Edition*, translated by Edmund Keeley and Philip Sherrard, edited by George Savidis. Translation copyright © 1975, 1992 by Edmund Keeley and Philip Sherrard. Princeton University Press; **Cawood, Aaron:** 'Playground Games' and 'Non-Binary Completionist' Reproduced by permission of the author; **Chan, Mary Jean:** 'Practice' from Flèche (Faber and Faber, 2019) Reprinted by permission of the Faber and Faber Ltd; **Chen, Chen:** 'i love you to the moon &' Originally published in The Academy of American Poems *Poem-a-Day*, then included in *Explodingly Yours* (Ghost City Press, 2023). Reprinted with permission of the author; **Chen, Winter:** '#131 Lapras' and '1D3N+1+Y' Reproduced by permission of the author; **Clancy, Sarah:** 'Ringing in Sick to go Mermaid Hunting' First Published in 2012 in *'Thanks for Nothing Hippies'* by Sarah

Nottingham, 2002) and 'To a Son Growing Up' originally published in *Torso* by Robert Hamberger (Redbeck Press, Bradford, 2007). Reproduced by permission of the author; **Hoffman, Richie:** 'Things That Are Rare' from *A HUNDRED LOVERS: POEMS* by Richie Hofmann, copyright © 2022 by Richie Joseph Hoffman. Used by permission of Alfred A. Knopf, an imprint of the Knopf Doubleday Publishing Group, a division of Penguin Random House LLC. All rights reserved; **Hughes, Langston:** 'Tired' from *The Collected Poems of Langston Hughes*. Reproduced by kind permission by David Higham Associates; **Hulme, Jay:** 'Jesus at the gay bar' and 'Don't die' from *The Backwater Sermons* by Jay Hulme. Reprinted by permission of Hymns Ancient and Modern; **Jarret, Keith:** 'A Gay Poem' copyright © Keith Jarrett, reproduced by kind permission by David Higham Associates; **Jones, Caitlin Tina:** 'You didn't go to prom with me' Reproduced by permission of the author; **Kay, Jackie:** 'Something Rhymed' Darling: New & Selected Poems (Bloodaxe Books, 2007) by permission of the publisher. Reproduced with permission of Bloodaxe Books. www.bloodaxebooks. com @bloodaxebooks (twitter/facebook) #bloodaxebooks; **Keohane, William:** 'Top surgery' First published in *Poetry Ireland Review*, Issue 134, Sept 2021. Reproduced by permission of the author; **Knights, Karl:** 'Skin Tags' First published in *The Ending Hasn't Happened Yet* (Sable Books, 2022) and 'A Room of Firsts'. Reproduced by permission of the author; **Ladin, Joy:** 'Survival Guide' first appeared in *Coming to Life* and was later included in *The Future is Trying to Tell Us Something: New and Selected Poems*, both from Sheep Meadow Press. Reproduced by permission of the author; **Liu, Timothy:** 'All Trains Are Going Local' from *Don't Go Back to Sleep*. Copyright © 2014 by Timothy Liu. Reprinted by permission of Saturnalia Books; **Lock, Jaime:** 'Mirror Boy' first appeared in *Giving Room* Mag Issue 1. Reproduced by permission of the author; **Lorde, Audre:** By permission of Abner Stein, 'A Litany for Survival', The Black Unicorn by Audre Lorde; W. W. Norton & Company © 1978, 1992 by Audre Lorde; **Ly, David:** 'Tips to Begin With' and 'The Trick' Reproduced by permission of the author; **Mayer, So:** 'We Are Librarian' is excerpted from the story 'green children', first published in *Truth & Dare* (Cipher Press, 2023), with thanks to Cipher. Reproduced by permission of the author; **McCann, Mícheál:** 'Immanence' Originally published in *Keeper*, Fourteen Publishing, 2022; **McCullough, John:** 'I am the Mob' Reprinted by permission of the author, 'Spout' from Reckless Paper Birds, Penned in the Margins, 2019, reproduced by permission of the publisher; **McLane, Maureen N.:** 'Syntax' From What I'm Looking For by Maureen N. McLane published by Penguin Press. Copyright © Maureen N McLane, 2008, 2010, 2014, 2016, 2017, 2019. Reprinted by permission

Young Person . . .' from *Limbic* by Peter Scalpello (Cipher Press, 2022) reprinted by permission of the author; **Smith, Chloe**: 'Not Quite Yet' Reprinted by permission of the author; **Soto, Christopher**: 'All the Dead Boys Look Like Me' from *Bullets into Bells: Poets and Citizens Respond to Gun Violence*. Copyright © 2017 by Christopher Soto. Reprinted by permission of the author; **Summers, Aidan**: 'Positive Visibility' Reproduced by permission of the author; **Taylor, Rosamund**: 'Sheep's Head Peninsula' Reproduced by permission of Banshee Press; **Tempest, Kae**: 'Flight' from *Divisible by Itself and One* by Kae Tempest copyright © Kae Tempest, 2023, published by Picador, reproduced by kind permission by David Higham Associates. **Thornber, Alex**: 'The Unknown' Reproduced by permission of the author; **Torchinsky, Sasha**: 'Gender Keeps Me Up At Night' and 'Erased' Reproduced by permission of the author; **Trott, Phoebe**: 'Exqueerience' Reproduced by permission of the author; **Verdi, Jess**: 'Briefly, there were books' Reproduced by permission of the author; **Vuong, Ocean**: 'Not Even' from *Time is a Mother* by Ocean Vuong published by Jonathan Cape. Copyright © Ocean Vuong, 2022. Reprinted by permission of The Random House Group Limited; **Wilson, Elspeth**: 'Eating Slurs for Breakfast', 'In Sims I Woohoo with a Girl' and '60% of Bisexual People are in Psychological Distress at Any One Time' were originally published in *Too Hot to Sleep*, published by Written Off Publishing. Reproduced by permission of the author; **Woods, Gregory**: 'Boys in Moonlight Shine' and 'Sunday Lunch' from *We Have the Melon*. Reprinted by permission of Carcanet Press; **Woolf Freja Nicole**: 'Rain Kiss' Reproduced by permission of the author.

Compiler Acknowledgements

Pulling an anthology together is no easy task. Thank you to every single poet who responded to my email and DM and who reacted so wonderfully to the idea of this project. It is such an honour to read, compile and edit your words; and it has been an even bigger honour getting to discover a whole new tranche of queer voices. Thank you for allowing me to work with you, and to share your words with the world. There is a community out there just waiting to discover you, and it is very much my hope that your words will find those readers at a time where they might need them the most.

Thank you, firstly, to the incomparable Gaby Morgan; you are, without a doubt, a powerhouse of a publisher, a dream of a mentor, an inspiration, a shining beacon, a colleague, and a friend. A big thank you to the equally dreamy Rachel Vale, who outshines every expectation. Every. Single. Time. You've created a package for this book that is everything it needed to be. Thank you for your constant and unwavering support. Thank you to Louisa Cusworth, for the insurmountable amount of paperwork necessary to making this book a real thing; I appreciate you. Thank you also to Tracey Ridgewell, Sue Mason, and Amy Boxshall, for even more behind-the-scenes work on this book. And, of course, to the whole Macmillan Children's team, for believing in this project and getting it out there.